## REVIEWS FOR

"THE HEAVENLY BEINGS that viewing other more perfect beings for the role of Messiah. Personally, I felt that the main character, Yoseph, in the book would be more qualified to lead us into the Messianic Age because of his imperfections and lessons that he experienced through his life. As I read *Messiah Interviews* I learned so much about biblical events and about my own spiritual beliefs. Previously, I had no knowledge about the Shechinah Third Temple, and limited knowledge of the Old Testament. It was also interesting for me to learn more about Jewish beliefs. I feel that my knowledge has greatly increased since reading this book, and I find myself interested in learning more.

The author, Jerry J. Pollock, is a man of science. It was fascinating to see how he combined his scientific knowledge with his spiritual beliefs. This made him even more credible in my eyes. As Yoseph was interviewed, he teaches us through his answers. As I was contemplating his responses to some very in-depth questions, I found myself questioning what my own personal responses would be. I found this to be especially true when I read his answers regarding the Ten Commandments. I found the *Messiah Interviews* by Jerry J. Pollock, Ph.D., to be profoundly thought-provoking and feel that readers who are on their spiritual journey will truly benefit from having read this book."

*Paige Lovitt, Reader Views*

"I WHOLE-HEARTEDLY RECOMMEND my good friend Jerry Pollock's *Messiah Interviews*. Although Jerry's expertise in secular science and psychoanalysis and my expertise in Chassidic Rabbinics does not necessarily allow us to share the same theological outlook in life, I so respect Jerry's quest for truth and his longing to see the Moshiach (Messiah); so much so that I sincerely hope the *Messiah Interviews* serves as an inspiration to all."

*Lubavitch Rabbi Adam Stein, Chabad at Stony Brook University*

"A UNIQUE AND REVEALING BOOK. I found the biographical events to be very interesting and revealing once I completely understood them. The interview form that the majority of the book is written in is definitely unique and creative. I enjoy the fact that the author tied true biographical events and self discovery into the process as it made for very interesting reading. *Messiah Interviews: Belonging to God* is recommended for those who enjoy books on religion, spirituality, and self-examination, intermixed with the element of fiction."

*Kam Aures, RebeccasReads*


"WHAT LIES IN THE FUTURE OF HUMANITY after it breathes its final breath? *Messiah Interviews: Belonging to God* is Jerry Pollock's spiritual journey of dealing with the uncertainty of what awaits him at the ultimate end of the road. Calling for readers to make their own choices, he offers his opinion on the matter and hopes to give food for thought when deciding. *Messiah Interviews* is a different sort of book on the afterlife, highly recommended."

*Midwest Book Review*


"A BOOK THAT ASKS US TO REFLECT on our values and make a positive contribution to the world. In the *Messiah Interviews: Belonging to God*, the main character, Yoseph readily confesses his limitations to his biblical interviewers—the angel Gabriel, Methuselah, Chanoch, Seth, King David, Moses, Jacob, Abraham and the prophet Isaiah— making amends for past discretions. What follows is a poignant and engaging conversation that challenges readers to look honestly at their flaws, examine their assumptions, values and beliefs, and be guided by a Higher source. In telling the story, Pollock explores both his intellect and his heart. If this leads to personal growth and reflection, then the *Messiah Interviews* will have fulfilled its goal."

*Miriam Leventhal, Feathered Quill Book Reviews*

"THERE ARE NO COINCIDENCES FOR PEOPLE who possess qualities of faith and righteousness. Nor can there be random chance happenings for those whom G-d has chosen for special treatment, and, perhaps a special purpose, writes author, scientist and seeker Jerry Pollock. Thus the reader is challenged to ask, Could it be me? Do I qualify? Do I qualify as a good person in God's Eyes to be part of the Messianic Age? The author has spent his life giving back. His journey is shared with you, the reader of *Messiah Interviews*. It is this reviewer's opinion that if you are a seeker with time to read only one book, that book must be *Messiah Interviews*."

*Richard Fuller, Metaphysical Reviews*

"*Messiah Interviews: Belonging to God* IS A TOUR-DE-FORCE that asks its readers to look at their own religious beliefs, to question and reaffirm those beliefs, and to understand the history behind their religious faith. Christian readers will find themselves with a clearer understanding of Judaism and its role as the basis of Christianity. Questions of science and religion's compatibility are deftly explored. Pollock writes with humor, attention to detail and tradition, and above all, with reverence for the human spirit and its never-ending quest to understand God. *Messiah Interviews: Belonging to God* is the perfect gift for anyone seeking a deeper spiritual journey."

*Irene Watson, Reader Views*

"AS WE READ JERRY J. POLLOCK'S *Messiah Interviews: Belonging to God*, it becomes quite evident that this is undoubtedly a most remarkable tome, something with its unique creativity and profound thought that is poles apart from the multitude of books concerning spirituality and religion. Using the mechanism of interviews with an outstanding biblical interview team, Pollock embarks on an insightful self-analysis dealing with a multitude of truth-seeking questions. His dexterity in revealing his own character in small fragments as well as the interlacing of insightful reflection makes for a captivating read. Moreover, his elegant prose hits us with immense energy as we muse over the many questions that the protagonist, Yoseph, is called upon to answer. By the time, you're done reading this intelligent narrative, you may even believe the Messiah Interviews actually happened."

*Norm Goldman, Book Pleasures*

"*Messiah Interviews* IS AN INTERESTING MIX OF FACT AND FICTION. Science and biblical history are woven together with a healthy dose of make believe to create a world where the main character, Yoseph, has the opportunity to vie for the job of the Messiah...but only if he makes it through his biblical interviews. Some of the best portions of Messiah Interviews comes from when Yoseph is between interviews and gets a chance to spend time with his wife, Marcia. Pollock's vivid details during these encounters are well done. The reader immediately feels transported to the time and place with them. The ending is superbly done and made it well worth the reading of the book."

*Cheryl Malandrinos, The Book Connection Blog*

"THE WILL OF GOD IS MIGHTIER THAN ANY FORCE ON EARTH. There are no coincidences for people who possess qualities of faith and righteousness. No chance happenings for those whom God has chosen. *Messiah Interviews: Belonging to God* is a well-written, insightful book that will get you to stop and mediate on the things of God. Someone who has suffered horrifically has the potential through their suffering to look inside and understand human nature. These are the deep thinkers and the ones most likely to see beyond the 'surface' of situations and uncover hidden truths. This job as earth's Messiah, the King of Israel would give closeness to the creator God—unimagined and unparalleled."

*Connie Harris, TCM Reviews*

"*Messiah Interviews* is a story of fiction, just written in a way that 'teaches and guides the reader,' rather than just telling a story. The author, Jerry Pollock, Ph.D., writes in a beautiful way—his words are prose upon paper. Messiah Interviews is a memorable and touching story. Readers are taken beyond the realm of the here and now and led to a place where they are enabled to search within themselves. This is a story that could easily be read and reread, with new things discovered with each reading."

*April Pohren, Café of Dreams Blog*


"WHAT AN ORIGINAL CONCEPT FOR A BOOK. After reading *Messiah Interviews*, I learned a lot about Jewish history and Judaism's interpretation of the End of Days. The concepts were thought-provoking. The biblical interviewers did not come off as fake but as true. They kept pushing Yoseph until they got him to see what they wanted him to see. I am looking forward to reading Jerry Pollock's first book, *Divinely Inspired: Spiritual Awakening of a Soul.*"

*Lissa Oehlberg, Reading Mama Blog*


"TO SAY THIS IS AN INTERESTING READ IS AN UNDERSTATEMENT. The questions posed by the biblical sages are extremely interesting as are the answers given by the main character. And as such, *Messiah Interviews* carries along nicely and entertains as well as instructs in biblical history and particulars of Torah. Is our hero the chosen Messiah once his spiritual mission on Earth finished? Or has Pollock too closely fused fiction with aspiration in his 'not so fictional' novel. I ask the reader to be his own judge and set my lens aside. In any case, *Messiah Interviews* is an interesting read and well worth the time to ponder the questions it introduces and to answer its call for a closer relationship with God during our lifetime now."

*Chris Querry, My Shelf Reviews*

**Also by Jerry Pollock, PhD**

*Divinely Inspired: Spiritual Awakening of a Soul*

∾ MESSIAH INTERVIEWS ∾

# MESSIAH
# INTERVIEWS
## Belonging to God

# JERRY POLLOCK

sHecHinaH third temple, inc.

Copyright © 2009 by Jerry J. Pollock, Ph.D.

Published by Shechinah Third Temple, Inc.

ISBN, Softbound Edition: 978-0-9817212-0-0

Library of Congress Control Number: 2008903194

Publisher's Cataloging-in Publication

Pollock, Jerry J. (Jerry Joseph), 1941-

    Messiah interviews: belonging to God / Jerry J. Pollock. -- 1st ed. - Boynton Beach, FL : Shechinah Third Temple, Inc., c2009.
      p. ; cm.
      ISBN: 978-0-9817212-0-0
      Includes bibliographical references.
      1. Judgment of God--Fiction. 2. Messiah--Judaism. 3. Messianic era (Judaism)--Fiction. 4. Heaven--Fiction. 5. Temple of Jerusalem (Jerusalem) 6. Spiritual life. I. Title.

PS3616.O5696 M47 2009      2008903194     813.6--dc22 0901

Book Design: Patricia Bacall
Cover Design: Magnus Andersson
Author Photo: Magnus Andersson

KING SOLOMON'S
WRITINGS FROM
THE BOOK OF PROVERBS

PROVERBS 8

*"I love those who love Me, and those who search
for Me shall find Me."*

*"For one who finds Me has found life."*

*My Marcia*

*To a truly remarkable woman, wife,
mother, and spiritual best friend. There is
none like you, and I am so lucky and
grateful that you are mine. You are my
bashert, my destiny.*

*My Creator*

*I ask that You be with me always.
Thank You for turning my life around and
lifting me heavenward. I love You.*

*Somewhere over the rainbow*
**Judy Garland**

# ∽ PUBLISHER'S NOTE ∾

All of the first chapters, with the exception of the My Blue Heaven chapter in the Yesterday section, refer to true biographical events. The biblical characters described in the Today and Tomorrow sections are humans and angels of the Hebrew Bible. The Messiah Interviews that the protagonist has with these famous individuals have never taken place, as they are the creation of the author.

The author's ideas on admission into the Messianic Age and his original interpretations on what's written about the Messiah or the Hebrew Bible should not be viewed as absolute truths. Where supporting information from biblical sages has been used in the text, the author has indicated their comments in quotation marks. However, whatever opinions the author cites, his own or that of others, should be considered to be what they are: opinions.

For further correspondence, contact Shechinah Third Temple, Inc:

Tel: 561-735-7958
Fax: 561-738-1535
Email: thirdtemple@bellsouth.net
Web: www.shechinahthirdtemple.org
www.thirdtempleinfo.com

# ༄ ACKNOWLEDGMENTS ༄

My Creator is my hero, and yet, I know Him not.

I am eternally grateful to my wife, who is my soul mate and anchor in life, as well as my parents, Anne and Jack Pollock, who gave me life. I also want to acknowledge Norm, who was everything I could hope for in a brother; I miss him very much. My maternal grandparents, Sam and Rose London, and my paternal grandmother, Lily Pollock, nourished my beginnings so that I could blossom later in life.

My children, Kenneth, Melanie, Seth, Sean, and Erin, and my extended family, Karen, Magnus, and Martha Jean, are a joy to me, as are my grandchildren, Sarah, Ethan, and those yet to be born. I am proud of all of them.

My son-in-law, Magnus Andersson, of Innervision Design, is responsible for the cover design. He gives me much more than his wonderful creativity, as does Sean Pollock, who did the original logo for our Shechinah Third Temple, Inc. nonprofit organization and publishing company. A trademark patent has been obtained for our logo.

I want to thank my exceptional editors, Pamela Guerrieri and Abiola Sholanke-Fluker, of Proofed to Perfection. They are beyond amazing. I am very fortunate to have Patricia Bacall of Bacall Creative, who did a wonderfully splendid job on the interior design of the book. It was a caring and talented Patricia who referred me to Pamela and Abiola. All three have made this book what it is.

I owe an enormous debt of gratitude to my primal therapist, Theresa Sheppard Alexander, who has never wavered in helping me resolve the tortuous twists and turns of my neurotic upbringing and adult life. I can't thank her enough. I thank John Speyrer, who publishes a Primal

Therapy Web page, for his insights into twin pregnancies. I am also grateful to Yvette Ducorsky for her friendship and spiritual advice. The kindness of Rabbi Adam Stein of Stony Brook University will not be forgotten. Rabbis Simon Jacobson's and Moshe Zauderer's online forums have offered me exceptional wisdom. I have also matured in my spiritual development from reading the insightful biblical commentaries of the rabbis at Mesorah Publications and from Rebbe Schneur Zalman's *Lessons in Tanya*. I wish I would have known the late Rabbi Menachem Mendel Schneerson, also known as "The Rebbe."

My close friends and relatives are always in my heart, as are my Ph.D. and dental students and academic mentors. I am saddened that some of my mentors have died, but I hope to see them in the Messianic Age. I want to pay tribute to the great men and women of the Hebrew Bible, who not only have been a part of history but also have created history. I am so very fond of the ancients, whom I look upon as kindred spirits. I often envision myself with the Israelites, crossing the Sea of Reeds during the Exodus from Egypt.

Finally, anyone who reads this book and then goes on to improve his or her character needs to be commended. God gives us a whole lifetime to make spiritual changes in our lives.

# Yesterday

# 1

# 2006—THE PHONE CALL

*IT WAS A WARM OCTOBER* afternoon in Boynton Beach. The heavens were a perfect linen blue with geometric insertions of amorphously shaped puffy, pure-white clouds. The sight of it all captured our love, from the very first moment we gazed at the Florida sky. After experiencing the extended summer months of seemingly never-ending, monotonous, moist heat, transplanted New Yorkers, like Yinnon and I, actually relish Florida weather even when the world around us is collapsing.

Yinnon claimed that it must have been his ancient Jewish ancestral genes, because he always liked heat and had an acrimonious distaste for the cold. I reminded him of course that his body temperature charted almost two degrees below normal and that the *raison d'être* could be the blame for his feeling cold. After all, I was the biochemist, and I confidently explained that enzymes lose four percent of their biological activity for every degree loss of body temperature. With as much bravado as I could muster, I proclaimed victoriously, "You see Yinnon, your enzymes are just not at peak, and consequently you can't possibly generate enough of your own body heat." Yinnon then smiled lovingly and said, "Yoseph, do you remember the winters growing up in Toronto, with near-frostbitten toes and fingers?" How could I forget? We walked to school and carried our books without gloves, and back in those days, we wore unlined black rubber boots that kept the snow out, but the cold in.

Our feet would freeze, yet he never complained. In fact, Yinnon never expressed any of his feelings in those early days. As the years past, his repressed anger, the hidden cause of his severe migraines, kept building to volcanic proportions.

We did learn one winter trick, which was really not a trick at all. When the wind whistled its eerie tune and hammered our entire beings, we would partially shield ourselves by walking sideways, or in blinding desperation, backwards. The only thing that mattered to him on those blustery days, was to focus solely on reaching his destination—school or home. However, he wasn't particularly enamored by the choice of either supposed sanctuary. This was because, although he didn't know it at the time, he was afraid of feeling the hopelessness of failure; and home ... well home just wasn't a safe place for him. Most of his early life, and even his entire life, can be summarized in three phrases: physical pain, emotional mental suffering, and the struggle-survival syndrome. I felt his Primal Pain, for he was my best friend and the lost brother that haunted my dreams. It was as if we emerged out of the same womb, and whatever pierced his soul caused my soul to bleed.

On that October 26th afternoon in 2006, we were sixty-five years old. As Yinnon recounted his tale, here he was staring nervously at both his watch and the phone. Each time he had a Primal Therapy session with Tracee, it was always the same anticipatory anxiety. The time on his watch was approaching 4 p.m. He took a gulping breath, picked up the phone, and dialed. He had been doing the therapy, off and on, since the early 1980s. Some might say that this was a long time, and I would have to concur. However, given his handicaps, which were imprinted so early in his mother's womb and then showcased in an indelible ugly neurosis in the afterbirth, he probably never should have had any semblance of inner peace in his primordial existence. Without his G-d-given intelligence, therapy, and the Creator coming into his life and bringing him gifts of Divine Providence, there would have been no hope.

"Hello! Hello Tracee! Hi Yinnon!"

## 2

# THE HOLY LAND

*WHILE YINNON WAS CONVERSING* with Tracee, I drifted back to memories of our time in Israel. The sounds of the guns that night reminded me of the firecrackers Yinnon and I would toss at each other when we were kids. In our secretive contests, Yinnon always held onto his firecrackers longer. Though he was neurotic and damaged goods, I was the scaredy cat, while he seemed to enjoy tempting fate and taunting me.

In 1967, Israel was in a grim Middle East war with its neighbors, Egypt, Syria, and Jordan, and we were huddled together alongside our Israeli neighbors in the basement of our duplex apartment building at 10 Ben Yehuda Street in Rehovot. There was no chatter that night, nor was there the option of sleep. My eardrums vibrated with the decibels of distant gunfire, which seemed just a little too close for a war novice like myself.

In our makeshift cramped basement shelter, it seemed as if life had flipped us irreversibly, and then had come to an immobilized standstill. All was motionless and dark. Only breath was moving, while time and space were hanging in a vacuum. Not a peep could be heard.

My mind had to do something—anything to get my body through the uncertainty and fear brewing in these tiny dark quarters of unlikely bedfellows. I purposely returned to biblical times, visually imagining what must have been an enormously, speechless crowd reaction. The Israelites were hard at war with the idol-worshipping Canaanites when the prophet Joshua emboldened with the power of G-d made the sun stand still, for all to see. Joshua, through the Omnipotence of the L-rd G-d, had openly defied and altered the laws of nature, the natural order of things—what is referred to in faith circles as Divine Providence. Needless to say. this was quite a miraculous event.

Many years later after returning from Israel, there was a time in my own life when I was to indirectly witness a paranormal incident that would shake free any doubts I had about G-d.

I was looking for something to watch on television one evening. I flipped the TV channels and stopped at *Larry King Live*. His guest that night was an attractive middle-aged British woman, who claimed to be a necromantic, a person who has the power to contact the dead. She was taking phone calls, and reaching trance-like states to connect with callers' dead relatives. One of the phone calls was from a mother who was grieving over the loss of her infant son. After a few moments in a sublime meditative state, the British woman made contact with the mother's son, and began to open and close her hand in the direction of the TV screen, repeating the word … love … love … love. At one point in the show, I chuckled, as Larry King frantically waved his hands in the air above, and asked, "Where are they?" He was trying to touch the spirits of the dead—of course, to no avail. I reflected on what I had observed, and spoke aloud, "That's neat." I went to bed, and thought no more of this mystical TV episode; that is, until the surprise of the next day.

At the appointment at my Long Island holistic doctor's office, I found myself talking with a woman, whom I previously shared conversations with, while we were each hooked up on our intravenous lines. I was into this nutritional stuff beginning in the early 1990s, and I had all of my silver mercury amalgam fillings in my teeth replaced with porcelain. As a scientist, I knew that there would be a lot of ingestion of the mercury during the dental procedures, and thus I elected to have intravenous treatment to remove any mercury, no matter the source, out of my body cells. It took twenty-six weekly treatments, followed by oral chelation, to eliminate all the mercury in my cells, as carefully measured by blood and urine analyses. The woman next to me, to whom I was speaking, was having EDTA treatments for her heart. She paused, and then asked, "Did you happen to see *Larry King Live* last night?" "As a matter of fact, I did," I replied. The woman then asked, "Do you remember the clasping and unclasping of the hands, and the repetition of the word *love*?" "Yes," I responded enthusiastically. Then she said, "That little boy was my grandson. That's how he motioned all the time, and the caller was my daughter. We have been sad for the longest time, because we lost such a special child, filled with love."

I was speechless. This woman was a very nice person, and she had no reason to lie. I realized that this was no coincidence. I was meant to be a part of this unusual happening. I was being shown something quite remarkable. G-d had created an interesting, dynamic world in which people were given gifts of contact with the dead, extrasensory perception, the odd ability to connect with ghosts and spirits, past lives, UFO experiences, etc. As the years have passed, I have come to believe in all of these mystical concepts, with the proviso that each person's gift can only be theirs, if they are worthy, and if G-d so chooses to endow them. Those who are not worthy in G-d's Eyes may believe they possess the gift, but in fact, they do not. In biblical days, the Hebrew prophets spoke the truthful word of G-d, and their prophecies were always precisely accurate, unlike that of the famous Nostradamus, who would be an example of someone we think of as an icon, but who actually was not. Some of the true prophets, like Joshua, could achieve supernatural status and make the sun stand still. The prophet Elijah was able to revive Jonah from the dead, because G-d needed Jonah for a higher purpose still to come. In the case of UFOs, my own personal belief is that, where legitimate, the spaceships are being flown by angels. Wild! Crazy! But can anyone disprove me? The Will of G-d is mightier than any force on earth, including the most potent nuclear power that man will be able to muster today and in future generations.

Momentarily, I was returned to the darkness and the stillness of the black night by the distant gunfire of the Six-Day War at hand. After the sounds quieted, my mind wandered off once again. I recalled our days at the Canadian Pharmacy School. Yinnon and I were both in the first year of our masters degree research studies and were residing on St. George Street in a shabby basement apartment, within ten minutes' walking distance of the university. We had a tough biochemistry exam the next day, and I was studying, but Yinnon was not. He told me that he had the most excruciating of headaches and was not able to prepare for tomorrow. He said that he would probably fail, which only exacerbated his pain. We were both "A" students, and for the very first time, academic failure was knocking at our door. It was too late to call in sick. In a little while, Yinnon fell asleep. He was out for perhaps no more than a half hour, when he awoke. "Yoseph, I'm completely free of pain," he uttered. "This has never happened to me. It's impossible." He returned to his studies, and he ended up receiving the highest grade on the exam. Back then, I would have said that this was a coincidence, but not today. There are no coincidences for people who possess qualities of faith and righteousness. Nor can there be random chance happenings

for those whom G-d has chosen for special treatment and, perhaps, a special purpose. Yinnon was to fall into the latter category. He seemed to be selected on High.

You might think that Yinnon and I were simply secular, spiritually bankrupt Jews; however, there were only partial truths to this statement. We had grown up hanging stockings on Christmas Eve, and we attended Jewish school where we learned to read and write Hebrew without understanding what we read. Our Bar Mitzvah preparation was mainly an exercise in rote. There was neither discussion of Jewish history nor culture by either our rabbi teacher or by our parents. The only Jewish holiday we were aware of was Passover, but even this was minimized. Yet, within the mix of a semi-secular upbringing, our experiences in Israel ignited something inside of us. This something is often referred to in Jewish Orthodox circles as the *pintele yid* (Jew), which keeps the sparks of our Judaism alive in a dormant state, so much so that deep down we inexplicably and unknowingly have faith and believe in G-d. Incredible miracles were to occur in later years; in fact, even before Yinnon's birth, such miracles spared and ultimately salvaged his life. Yinnon had been a neurotic sinner, a tortured prisoner of his own mind, and I was fearful that ultimately he would have been institutionalized, had it not been for Divine benevolence.

Yinnon used to paint this wonderful picture of his upbringing, telling me how great his parents were, but I knew better. I knew the saddest of hidden truths. When we were kids, we used to nervously laugh about Toronto's 999 Queen Street, the lunatic asylum. In those days, it really was the actress Olivia DeHaviland's *Snakepit* movie, for those of you who are old enough to remember. You went into the nut house, and never came out. The inmates were crazy, or were they? Little did I know that Yinnon's entire being was to unravel and shatter into a thousand pieces. He was to discover the bitter reality of his childhood neurosis in Primal Therapy at age forty, and then later, and much more ominous, he would sink into the black hole of bipolar disorder at age fifty.

The next morning, dawn's light had displaced the darkness, as the radio announcer jubilantly asserted that Israeli mirage jets had flown below the radar and taken out the entire Egyptian air force. As Ph.D. students and foreigners at the Weizmann Institute of Science, we were advised to leave the country before the war began, but we had courageously elected to stay. We had rolled hard fours, and enjoyed the psychedelic high of victory. We weren't just bystanders anymore. We felt we earned the right to finally belong. It was perhaps the most gratifying and defining moment of our stay in Israel, although our heroics went unnoticed. After all, we were Jews, and that's what we are supposed to do. We line up behind the State of Israel in times of peril, but we have long forgotten how to line up behind G-d.

Yinnon and I had won Special Canadian Student Scholarships to study anywhere in the world, and because we were blood brothers and did everything together, we chose Israel when Harvard turned us down. Atypically, I charted the way. I had a yearning to discover something of my Jewish heritage. I was an academic at heart, and have always had this passionate penchant and fervor to learn and absorb everything that I can about any topic that I study. I was totally ignorant of my ancestry. My alter ego, my lost twin, was for a change, the tail that wagged the dog.

# 3

# DIAMOND IN THE ROUGH

*THERE ARE TWO KINDS OF* rubble. One that you visualize with your eyes, which cannot be mistakenly taken for anything except what your brain signals you to actually see. And the other, which your brain sees and records as magical, like a diamond in a pile of manure.

On the very day after the Six-Day War, we were to discover both kinds, although in 1967, neither of us were equipped with a discerning eye, because we didn't know "shoots from *shinola*," as far as our Jewish heritage was concerned. It was fifteen, then thirty years later, when we would realize and appreciate the awesomeness of that incredible day. Thirty years later, Yinnon and I would initiate a self-study of our Jewish roots, history, culture, and religion, which would permit us to fly on the wings of angels, heavenward, to the unknowable domain of the Creator.

Ilse, the heavily German-accented, always properly sophisticated lady, who was the Weizmann Institute's coordinator for foreign visitors had miraculously secured a bus for us to visit the gains of the spoils of war. With the rising sun, we traveled to our first stop, EL Arish on the Red Sea. Out of fear, I tried not to stare at the Arab inhabitants or their decrepit homes. Instead, I gazed at the purity of the gorgeous aquamarine color of the water. It was ironic that the water was so calm in a region so filled with man's hatred for man. The Holy Land is prophesied to be the Big Bang of all apocalypses, where destiny, judgment and justice will one day meet, and crown the winners and punish the losers for the past six thousand years. When we left the Gaza Strip for Jerusalem, I glanced out the window of the bus, and reflected on my favorite Shakespearian play, *Macbeth*. The opening poetic lines, which I still repeat to myself to this day, belong to three cackling witches with prophecies of their own.

> "*First Witch:*
>
>> *When shall we three meet again?*
>> *In thunder, lightning, or in rain?*
>
> *Second Witch:*
>
>> *When the hurly-burly's done*
>> *When the battle's lost and won.*
>
> *Third Witch:*
>
>> *There will be ere the set of sun.*
>
> *First Witch:*
>
>> *Where the place?*
>
> *Second Witch:*
>
>> *Upon the heath.*
>
> *Third Witch:*
>
>> *There to meet with Macbeth.*
>
> *First Witch:*
>
>> *I come Graymalkin!*

*Second Witch:*
> *Paddock calls.*

*Third Witch:*
> *Anon.*

*All:*

> *Fair is foul and foul is fair*
> *Hover through the fog and filthy air."*

Destiny, judgment, and justice, the metaphorical three witches who will meet not with the protagonist, Macbeth, but will rendezvous with G-d. When? "At the End of Days, a precursor to a different age for human beings." Where? "On the battlefields of Israel and Jerusalem." Who? "G-d will confront those, the seventy nations, according to the Hebrew Bible, who are not fair but are foul and who for centuries have been trying to destroy Israel." What? "Fairness and justice and judgment will prevail." Why? "Because destiny has always marched from the imperfection towards perfection, the Messianic Age, when G-d's presence will be as universal as the waters of the sea. Destiny, judgment, and justice are all part of G-d's master plan for humankind."

When the age of G-d arrives, signaling the age of the Messiah, it will come with the flaming passion of an unstoppable stampede.

Thirty years later, we would internalize the significance of what we saw in Jerusalem, the City of Peace, where heaven *once* met earth, when the First Temple, conceived by King David and built by his son, Solomon, stood on Mount Moriah. Israel, the Land given in a Covenant to the Patriarchs, Abraham, Isaac, and Jacob, had been regained militarily by secular Jews in 1948. Not Jerusalem, however, that is, until yesterday. Because secular Jews reclaimed the Land, there are many among ultraorthodox Jews, who to this day do not recognize the State of Israel.

When the First Temple fell to the Babylonians, the Divine Presence, the *Shechinah* or *Shekinah*, had departed on the wings of the conjugal *Cherubim* angels who guarded the Ark of the Covenant, the Holy Tablets of Civilization, the Ten Commandments. The downslide had continued until the Second Temple was destroyed in 70 C.E. by the Roman general Titus. The remaining Jews of the Twelve Tribes, mainly the Tribes of Judah and Benjamin as well as the Levites and *kohanim*, were scattered to the four corners of the earth to ensure Jewish survival, at least somewhere in the world if elsewhere, they were being persecuted and slaughtered. At the End of Days, it is prophesied that these Twelve Tribes will recreate the spiritual foundations of Judaism, which will ascend to heights more glorious than ever before. *"Incredible to Me,"* as G-d, the L-rd of Hosts, promises.

The sole protection of G-d's Covenant with the Patriarchs had been lost. The Jewish people had not been able to maintain the exalted spiritual doctrine of the Ten Commandments, even with centuries of warnings from the Hebrew prophets. Despite this loss, Yinnon and I were here at the gates of the Old City of Jerusalem, on the threshold of history, almost 2,000 years after the Jewish expulsion from the Holy Land.

We were met by a guide who led us through narrow alleyways, in what was once the hustle and bustle of the Jewish Quarter in the Old City. In the rubble of an Arab backyard, we came upon our ancient diamond in the rough—a very small stone wall no bigger than the familiar lane wall we used to play the game ledger on as children growing up in downtown Toronto. I remember the oddness and beauty of this naturally sculpted stone wall in this setting of row on row of Arab houses. It was the Wailing or the Western Wall, the only vestige remaining of the Second Temple, built by the return of a tiny percentage of dedicated Jews to Israel after the Babylonian exile.

Yinnon and I agree, in retrospect, that this auspicious visit to Jerusalem was the second high point of our belonging to Judaism and the Holy Land. However, we did not yet belong to G-d.

As we walked through the deserted Arab market, I was thinking, "Wow! This is the mystique of *Casablanca* with Humphrey Bogart and Ingrid Bergman, and my all-time favorite movie character actor, Sydney Greenstreet." Surprisingly, the shops were open for business, as if the violence of past days' fighting were invisible in this section of Old Jerusalem. I wondered how this could be? I was at a loss for a logical explanation.

Judging by the suspicious glares of the shopkeepers, who hadn't seen Jews in their midst in decades, a new era was dawning. Peace, however, would remain elusive. As we continued our walking, the guide stopped, and we gazed out onto a dusty mountain with splotches of grass and trees. This was not Mount Moriah, for it had long been buried underground with the First and Second Temples. Our knowledgeable guide said that this was the Mount of Olives, and the trees were olive trees. Yinnon, I know, felt very foolish and ignorant, when he was overheard calling it the Mound of Olives. He was a sensitive soul, and I could tell that this embarrassment would bother him for years to come.

The ride to Jericho was surprisingly boring; that is, until we came upon the foreign patch of greenery of this biblical city, set in the midst of sagebrush desert dust. It was strikingly majestic, as green as I remember the farms of northern Ontario or the rolling hills of Ireland and unlike anything I would have envisioned. It resembled the secluded oases depicted in those desperate desert scenes in the movies, where the brave hero is struggling to survive and is saved before succumbing to the desert sun. Yinnon whispered in my ear, "Enough with the movies, already." The odd camel even came into view from the bus window. And then the electrifying shock.

Rubble that your brain relayed to your eyes as real rubble and not diamonds in the unusual greenery of Jericho. The Palestinian refugee camps. Cardboard-like shacks that reminded me of the horizontally attached houses that I would build with decks of playing cards as a child. The refugee houses seemed as fragile as my house of cards. One gust of wind or a slight push of the hands, I felt, would crumble the whole structure. I was mortified that people lived this way. The only word in the English language that seems appropriate is *squalor*. I was glad to drive on; still, the memory has never left me. I grew up poor, but this was my first introduction to poverty. The beggars, panhandlers, and homeless in Toronto or Tel Aviv were a fact of life that I accepted as being part of life. Somehow, this scene was different and was reinforced even more when I later traveled to India. Where were my eyes all these years? Were they simply morphological structures in the sockets of my head? I wanted to feel the plight of this sorry lot of the human race, and I did, until …

Our final stop was the mountainous Golan Heights, and once again, we weren't at all prepared for what was about to unfold. Another embossed imprint in my overcrowded sad brain's memory bank. Syrian bunkers overlooking the Jewish Kibbutzim in the Sea of Galilee. The *kibbutzniks* below were sitting ducks. I turned to see Yinnon crouching, ready to heave. He pointed while holding his other hand over his mouth. I blankly gazed at the posters beside the bunkers. My eyes were transfixed on the pictures, and I was gasping to catch my breath. There in full battle fatigue were Syrian army soldiers using rifle bayonets to push frail, defenseless Jews wearing rags into the sea. I understood the horror in my eyes and once again internalized the meaning of hatred and anti-Semitism. It was a modest reminder of the unforgettable, tormenting, haunting pictures that I have seen in Holocaust museums.

It had been too long a day. The ride home was quietly innocuous, as people nodded off. At one point, the bus stopped roadside so that we could relieve ourselves. Boys to the right and girls to the left, with the bus acting as a barrier. This one memorable day shook Yinnon and me to our core. I felt spent, and I have returned to these scenes over and over again to play them in my mind, like the piano player, Sam, in the movie *Casablanca*. "Play it again Sam." Yinnon was likewise reliving the same script in his nightmares. I wondered if others on the bus were similarly affected. How could they not be? I wondered also if other Jews, who were not on this trip, would have been changed by the experience, as Yinnon and I were.

I once read that hearing or seeing something may not register in your mind. And even if it does, people usually come away with a completely different brain registration after listening to someone else's story or observing highly moving scenes. Some people only manage an anecdotal comment or two, while to others the whole experience is immediately forgotten. Only in exceptional instances does anything penetrate. The life of one person rarely changes anyone else's life, even when the circumstances being described are quite profound.

# 4

# TIME LINE REGRESSION
# JUNE 1981

*W*E WERE LIKE TWO PEAS in a pod. We had divorced our first wives, became professors at Stony Brook University on Long Island, and were living together in a summer cottage in the incorporated village of Poquott. Yinnon had been more interested in the neurosciences, in the workings of the human mind, while I chose the life of a microbiologist-biochemist with a pharmacology bent.

It was a Saturday night and we had finished our hamburgers and onion rings at the Good Steer restaurant, when Yinnon suddenly suggested that we go back to my office. He wanted to tell me about a new regressive therapy that he was experimenting with. Yinnon had suffered mild bouts of depression, and I was hesitant to comply with his request. He had walked on hot coals, explored New Age cults, and dabbled with deep meditative states. He was aware of my concerns, but he always blew me off. I would say, "Yinnon, you know much more than me. Nevertheless, you can't push the human mind to extremes without the supervision of a professional, and you are not a professional. I advise against wild experimentation and strongly urge you to maintain your brain balance. If your mind crosses over, you may be consumed and not be able to come back."

Thank G-d, he was not into hallucinogenic drugs. I reiterated stories of Aaron's two sons who had expired in attempting to flee their bodies with their souls. I told him that I thought that King Solomon was often moody and could barely control his highs and lows. I gave him my personal opinion of Jesus. Truly charismatic with goodness and kindness; however, he operated in a constant state of hypomania. So much so that he said that you had to go through him to get to heaven. "I am the Way." None of my glib rhetoric phased Yinnon. He replied, "Yoseph, I'll tell you what. This time I'll be the senior scientist and you'll be the subject." "Well thanks a lot, Yinnon. Now, you want my mind, like yours, to be blown apart like a cornucopia."

I turned the lock of the outside door, and we surreptitiously entered Building "L," Westchester Hall. No one was about. The building was abandoned, as all the expert-thinking scientific minds had taken their thoughts home for the weekend. We sat in my 10x10 cubicle of an office, and turned off the fluorescent lights. It was a warm, hazy, moonlit night, and I had had some red wine, probably too much, with dinner. I felt unusually relaxed and light-headed. Even thoughts of my research experiments had faded, which was a rare occurrence. Wherever I was or whatever I was doing, I would be thinking science. Science was my life, my first love. I Yoseph was going to win the Nobel Prize one day. Out of unconditional love for my friend, I was all ears and ready to focus.

*Yinnon:* Imagine you are parked on a deserted street. Not a soul is around, and you are sitting behind the driver's wheel looking up at the stars and the moonlit night. Now just breathe as slowly and deeply as you can.

*Yoseph:* Shall I remove my glasses?

*Yinnon:* Yes. Try to relax, and imagine leaving yourself in the car as you are now, but also take yourself across the street and sit down on the curb. Look at yourself in the car, from where you are sitting on the curb.

*Yoseph:* Is the me still in the car supposed to know that I am being observed by myself?

*Yinnon:* (Exasperated) Forget about the technical stuff. Just concentrate. If you want to both self-observe and self-remember, then fine. Let the heaviness depart from your body and try to sink down into a meditative state. Let all the tension in your body sink through your feet into the floorboard of the car. Permit yourself to enjoy this happy feeling. Let all your muscles relax.

I had meditated on several occasions, so I was confident that I knew how to do this. I felt my head tilting slightly to my left side, and I was freely secreting saliva from my parotid and submandibular-sublingual salivary glands, and I started to drool, familiar physiological characteristics of my altered meditative state.

*Yinnon:* Now, see yourself becoming light and shapeless, and freely floating out the window. You are flying upwards with absolutely no effort. You are as light as a feather. Let yourself fly. Let yourself go. Let your whole being rise to heaven.

And I allowed myself. And I flew upwards, higher and higher. I landed upright on a mountain, like Superman would land, and then found myself descending, carrying the Tablets of the Ten Commandments. I was Moses. I even looked like him, long white beard and robe. Standing at the foot of the mountain, just waiting to pounce upon me, were Israelites with hostile eyes. They were blocking my way, and I feared for my life. I began to move through the unyielding crowd and they reluctantly gave way. It was as if I was walking an

Indian gauntlet, trying to keep my composure, hold my breath, and simultaneously disguise my fear. I felt that they were ready to murder me. Then, in the distance I saw two smiling women. My faltering courage was fortified, and I felt a huge sigh of relief. I recognized my daughter Erin. The other girl had blondish-brown hair and was much taller than Erin, but I couldn't identify her at the time. I think I know, today, that the taller girl was my nine-year-old granddaughter, Sarah, all grown up. Both girls were biblically dressed like everyone else in this surreal scene. The two women wore *babushkas* or kerchiefs around there heads, like I remember both my grandmothers wearing. I pondered momentarily. Were they my wives in a past life, and not my daughter and granddaughter? My eyes opened.

There was a smile on my face and a feeling in my heart and soul of inner peace. When I described what I had experienced to Yinnon, he remained silent, but he wasn't smiling. I don't think even he expected a Moses time line regression from me. I detected his envy, and I quickly reassured him that none of this was real. However, I didn't convince him. How could I do that? I couldn't convince myself that what had just transpired wasn't true and that, indeed, I had been Moses in a past life.

I tried to change the course of our conversation and said, "I don't think it would be unreasonable that Moses would be frightened. After all, the Israelites had grown impatient while Moses had been on top of Mount Sinai. They had built the Golden Calf." Yinnon wasn't biting. It was as if I had stolen something from him. He became aloof, and our evening ended on a sour note.

All my earlier advice to Yinnon had gone by the wayside. I wanted desperately to believe that I had been Moses in another life. In 1983, Yinnon and I returned to Israel. The highlight of our trip was climbing Mount Sinai. We carried the *Challah,* and at the peak Yinnon and I chanted the Hebrew prayer blessing over the bread. I kept waiting for

something Divine to happen; however, it never did. I was disappointed. We both laughed as we descended the mountain, farting, and caught up with our small group at St. Catherine's Monastery. We had traveled by truck through the desert *wadis* and returned to Israel's Elat after a border check on the Egyptian side. Our Bedouin guide, Achmed, bid us goodbye, and I slipped him a tip. I also gave $40 American to our Egyptian guide, Jimmy, and asked him to buy us a painting in Cairo and send it to us in New York. The other Egyptian on the trip gave me a sideways kind of look that meant, "Are you a naive stupid jerk?" I scribbled down my address on a scrap piece of paper and, of course, never heard from Jimmy again.

5

# THE PHONE CALL
# OCTOBER 26, 2006

*"Never seek the wind in the field.*
*It is useless to try to find what is gone."*

*Y*INNON HAD IGNORED the conventional psychology and self-help wisdom and entered Primal Therapy in Manhattan with Tracee in August of 1981. He said that his daily living was mechanical and relegated to mostly feeling down. As his best friend since 1941, I had repeatedly observed him at close enough range to realize that he wasn't comfortable in his own skin. His mind seemed to be somewhere else, battling unknown demons that were trying to possess his inner soul. He found it hard to smile, not to mention belly laugh, which simply was not part of his physiology.

I admired my friend, Yinnon, and was proud of him. He was embarking on the road less traveled. Moreover, he was stepping forward with courageous honesty, freely admitting in 1981 that he never really felt joy, only less tension in his aching muscles. It was as if he was ready to begin his journey anew in the Promised Land after aimlessly wandering the past forty years in the wilderness. Yinnon's downward spiraling view on life brought sadness to my heart and tears to my eyes; yet, there was a fringe of hope and opportunity and bravery. A crack had been opened in the doom and gloom of his infinite darkness.

> *"Life's but a walking shadow, a poor player,*
> *That struts and frets his hour upon the stage,*
> *And then is heard no more, it is a tale*
> *Told by an idiot, full of sound and fury*
> *Signifying nothing."*

> *"The attempt and not the deed confounds us."*

> *"Cowards die many times before their death;*
> *The valiant never taste of death but once."*

> *"There is a tide in the affairs of men,*
> *Which taken at the flood, leads to fortune;*
> *Omitted, all the voyages of their life*
> *Is bound in shallows and in miseries.*
> *On such a full sea are we now afloat,*
> *And we must take the current when it serves,*
> *Or lose our ventures."*

I reminded myself that we were in the year 2006. I looked up at Yinnon, who was far away, somewhere in another world. It was like Yinnon had been smitten with epilepsy. He was just staring into space.

At that frozen moment, he seemed as unreachable as he was, when he was in an episode of his mania. He suddenly snapped to the present and unexpectedly blurted out a quote of George Santayara.

*"Those who do not remember the
past are condemned to relive it."*

I asked him what Santayara's quote meant to him? He replied, "I was born neurotic and will die neurotic, unless I remember and relive the past, exactly as it was back then, in order to expose my buried unconsciousness and transform it to consciousness."

"Oh, it's kind of like the destroyed remains of the First and Second Temples," I replied, "buried under the earth and waiting to be excavated."

"I guess, that would be a simple analogy," Yinnon said, "but what I am referring to goes far deeper than the surface of the skin. You have to peel the layers of the human mind, an essentially impossible task, like digging down to the most central point of the earth. At the central core of neurosis are, at first sight, the seemingly opposite beasts—the fear of not being wanted or loved and the need to be wanted and loved." However, as Tracee often states, "you need to peel all the layers of the onion skin. I've been at this, as you know for twenty-five years, and I am still peeling away the onion; although most of my neurosis has gone."

"What do you mean by neurosis?" I queried. Yinnon explained.

*Yinnon:* Neurotic is when you do not behave as who you are at your inner core. The premise for everything you do was imprinted in your brain long ago. As long as these imprints remain hidden in the unconscious, they create internal pressures. The painful energies of these pressures vigilantly keep knocking at your door and misguide you in a myriad of futile directions to search for loving, nurturing parents in all of your relationships in the present. I emphasize futile, analogous Yoseph to your Shakespeare's quote, 'Life's but a walking shadow.' If you could see yourself clearly in the mirror, beyond what your eyes see, you would realize that your parents were not loving and nurturing. And no matter what you do, and in your neurosis you will never give up trying to do, you can never change that reality.

In neurosis, you will like someone, even someone that you love, who meets your needs. However, as soon as that loving family member does not meet your neurotic needs, you won't like that very same person. Likely, he or she will make you angry, and while you will inevitably continue to have expectations externally from that person, you will be disconnecting internally and never go to the source of your emotional trauma. The anger becomes a defense mechanism for never reaching the imprints buried in your brainstem and limbic system, where the raw truths of the origins of your sadness, your hurts and needs of not being loved, lie. That deprivation of early love can never be fulfilled in the present, as long as it festers in every sinew and skeletal structure in your body. The best you can do is to have periods of less tension, but no inner peace will find you. Melancholia will instead haunt your being, and you will be like Prometheus caught up in endless agony. I would suggest reading Arthur Janov's works. He's the real maven and discoverer of Primal Therapy.

In the present, when an event in childhood or adulthood triggers a primal feeling, the neurotic doesn't know where the feeling comes from. He feels only relentless panic and anxiety in his body, and he dreads. He never feels the true feeling, for example, beneath his birth trauma because his sympathetic flight or fight reaction is in flight. The panic is also a defense mechanism, so that he doesn't have to deal with the possibility of dying. His body, soul, and mind are desperately running away from this awful trauma, which is threatening the very core of his survival, where death was imminently real.

By returning to the same scenes over and over again, for as long it takes, new insights and further tranquility will be ascertained, until all the layers of the onion skin are peeled away. In essence, it's like releasing or chiseling away small portions of the pain (the wood chips) associated with the total pain (the tree), a little bit at a time.

I wonder how many onions I have been peeling these last twenty-five years? A multitude, considering the number of daily traumas I have survived. More to go!

"Let's move on, so I can tell you the one salient result of my session with Tracee."

*Tracee:* Stay with the feeling Yinnon.

*Yinnon:* I seem to be rocking like a gentle swinging pendulum. Tiny, soft, shallow waves rocking me back and forth like sleeping on a boat moored at the dock. There is no separation of the gentle swaying and myself. We are one together. My eyes are open because colors are flashing before me. It's so peaceful, so wonderful. My first awareness of life: blissfully floating in the water. Then, Oh, my G-d! My back feels cool. The gentle rocking is disappearing and I can't get it back. Oh no!

The gentle rocking in the amniotic sac, the Garden of Eden? It was Yinnon's for the briefest of moments. Then it disappeared. So little, and not enough, has been the story of Yinnon's life. On reflecting on Yinnon's womb phone conversation, I was quietly thinking that those few seconds of magic were the only barrier to his becoming a sociopath. He couldn't figure out the significance of the cold back. He would soon solve the riddle.

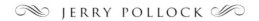

*"I'm cool and I travel up and down your body.*
*If you try and repress me, you'll have anxiety.*
*Who am I?"*
*He was to find out. "I'm FEAR of course."*

He told Tracee that in 1981, seven months before he began therapy with her, he was lying on his bed, and out of the blue said to me, "My mother doesn't love me." A coolness was felt throughout his body. He had admitted for the first time that his upbringing was not the Monet that he had painted for himself. When he had asked me what I thought the coolness was, I replied that I didn't know. However, now it all made sense to Yinnon. Further, he told Tracee, "I don't know if there is any relationship, but each time I get a similar cool chill in my back, a cold and sore throat come on. Maybe it's too much yin and not enough yang. I've never been able to get a good explanation from otolaryngologists. Neurosis equals stress. Stress damages your organs. Your organs, according to Chinese medicine, control your body heat. I may not have enough elemental wood to burn to make the fire."

As they analyzed the session, Tracee made two important comments to Yinnon. He had felt deeply, more deeply than ever before. Secondly, he was able to open his unconscious memory bank to his time in the amniotic sac, probably the result of his being so happy in his present life in Florida. His *Feng-Shui* house especially gave him joy, and he was grateful for so much that he had been blessed with.

6

# THE GARDEN OF EDEN
# OR EVIL?

*YINNON HAS ALWAYS BURIED* himself in a cerebral avalanche of thought. He felt in many ways, and I tended to agree that the chronological sequence of life should have been reversed, or at least modified. Ought not the Fifth Commandment be changed? Must it be a one-way street in which children honor their parents but parents do not cherish their children? And ought not children be able to start their lives off having some control of their own destiny, instead of becoming lost souls as a result of lack of control over who their parents turn out to be? It's easy to cry, "foul" or "sour grapes," and be labeled a complainer. However, the truth of the matter is that when you are born to dysfunctional parents, who may or may not, in turn, themselves have been born to dysfunctional parents, you pretty well remain a lifelong victim who spends his days in perpetual suffering. You are essentially a glossed-over casualty victim of war who has fought in a lopsided and unfair battle.

Yinnon often compared himself to the passenger pigeon. He quoted from the author of a poem, whose name he couldn't recall.

*"The passenger pigeon has become extinct, the bird of yesterday. All that's left is the encephalitis carrying, ugly creature, the common pigeon, who creeps around city hall steps on soot-stained feet."* Fortunately for Yinnon, he survived extinction.

Yinnon's journey has often made me think of T. S. Eliot's magnificent inspirational poem, which I identify with as my road in life.

> *"We shall not cease from exploration.*
> *And at the end of all our exploring,*
> *we will arrive where we started.*
> *And know the place for the first time."*

His quest became all-consuming. Emerge from the darkness into the light and finally find the elusive inner peace. Dream the impossible dream and fight the unbeatable foe.

Yinnon was a brilliant intellectual, and he knew the ins and outs of his aggravated mind. His problem was how to translate his thoughts into speech and action. He had suffered the destruction of too early a damage in the basilisk's den, his mother's womb, which was reinforced throughout his sixty-six years of life.

He should have succumbed in the serpent's hole, his mother's womb, but he survived because of Divine energy and intervention, or so he believed. Listen to his story and make up your own mind.

*Yinnon:* It must have been early on in the pregnancy, when I first became aware that I was alive. Of course, at that time, I, Yinnon, had no developed prefrontal cortex to tell me that life begins before birth. Nor was I able to assign the exact time periods for the events that I am about to describe. My later readings on the birth process would inform me of approximate dates, which I can now correlate with the events I experienced as a fetus in my mother's womb.

The gentle rocking of the Garden of Evil disguised itself as the Garden of Eden. The cool back signaled the key moment that would unveil the mask of the Garden of Evil, and forever transform my personality. Surprise! Surprise! I was startled. Like being shot by a stun ray gun, while simultaneously being pierced by the unexpected sting ray of a jelly fish. I was immobilized, frozen in time, like the evolutionary fossils of our ancient past. The best I could do was to barely open my mouth in fear, and snarl like an irritated dog that wants nothing more than to be left alone, but is instead bothered by human touch. In a matter of moments, the fear turned to terror, and I began to jostle about like a ball hitting the walls and ceiling of a squash court. Only, I was not on a gym court. I was in my bubble, the narrow confines of the amniotic sac. I did my best to express my displeasure by stretching my tightened face into a phony smile, akin to frowning. Momentarily, the jostling stopped and then began again. My dry mouth opened barely wide, and I screamed in silent horror.

When the jostling once again stopped, I tried desperately to get back to the gentle rocking of the Garden of Eden, but I could not. It was then that I felt spontaneous energy around me, guiding my arms and legs in what I would describe today as very slow Tai Chi movements in a warm pool of water.

Suddenly, my Tai Chi movements were interrupted. Though this time, my startled eyes were squinting to see another creature occupying the womb. He, I think it was a male twin, was staring right back at me with huge dark eyes. I don't think he was my identical twin, because he seemed to be occupying his own space. We must have been in the first trimester, since by eleven weeks, the eyelids usually fuse to close and protect the eyes until the seventh month, when the eyes open again. I was startled and fascinated, as my twin began to duplicate my own Tai Chi aerobics. We were like two copycat jugglers, or the dueling banjoes in the movie *Deliverance*. Very soon, my twin not only mimicked me exactly, he arrogantly went off by himself, and seemed to be performing his own version of Tai Chi aerobics.

Then came the bolt of lightning. My twin and I were being sucked out of the womb. The force was overpowering. I could see his terrified face. It was as if I was looking into a mirror seeing myself. I reached out with my hand to touch him. He made a feeble attempt to do the same. I felt his energy, and then he disappeared from view. I was fast following in my twin's footsteps, being pulled far to my right in a tug of war. Unexpectedly, I felt that energy again, but this time it was very strong, forcing me back to the left in the gentlest of motions, in a direction opposite to that of the suctioning vacuum.

I once asked my father, shortly before he died, if my mother had aborted any other children. My father looked me directly in the eyes and nodded yes, and I knew what he told me then was true. He said that my mother had aborted one child that he knew of, and sadly for him, it wasn't his. I suspect from his facial expression that she had also aborted his fertilized sperm.

It is said that G-d can save you from the forces of nature; yet, He does not interfere in the free will exercised by man against man. I adhere to this thinking, with the exception that His compassion can reverse intended outcomes through miracles, if He has a further purpose for a man to alter the course of world history, or more accurately, fulfill His plan for humankind. The first statement seems to be a truism, since even some of G-d's fiercely loyal Hebrew prophets were murdered, as was Jesus. And we are all aware of mass murder on the scale of the Holocaust.

The only explanation that makes sense to me is there shall be accountability for one's good and bad actions at the End of Days. A woman aborting, or attempting to abort, her child would seem to fall within this realm of man's action against man. In my case, I believe Divine Providence stepped in and interfered with the natural course of events. It wasn't the only time. I had other supernatural experiences later in life when G-d saved my life. Why me? He had His reasons. I had to find out for myself what my mission was.

The surest way today for a mother not to care about her unborn child is to either drink or smoke. My mother did both, as I suspect a large percentage of mothers did back then. I had been a half-a-pack smoker myself when I was a teenager, but had never gotten hooked.

My next surprise was astonishing. I was breathing in tobacco smoke as a fetus. Returning to the womb as an adult, I easily recognized the taste, and smelled the distinct odor of tobacco. I began to choke ferociously and cough silently in the amniotic sac. My first tobacco primal lasted several minutes. It was agony. I was responding to every puff. More cold back chills of terror came my way and spread to every part of my body. I was abound in awful panic. I was outmatched by a ruthless, merciless opponent, who didn't care about me. I was to revisit and relive the tobacco primals more than three dozen separate times, until the experience dissipated. I thought I knew suffering. The worst was yet to come.

I was in the birth canal being bounced from side to side against the womb walls like a ping pong ball. My head was vibrating in orbit, and too much was happening, too fast, all at once. The physical pain intensified. Over and over, I pulled inward, vainly trying to protect myself from being crushed, while simultaneously holding my breath for as long as I was able. My body was being crushed and torn apart, like being eaten alive, all without mercy from a mother who didn't want me and was giving it her last best shot to kill me. I was feeling this pain as an adult returning to his birth.

The feelings were all consuming and overpowering. Hundreds of times my body and brain spontaneously contracted in seizure-like movements or reverberations, where I momentarily lost my conscious awareness of what just happened. During these periods, which would last for up to thirty seconds and sometimes longer, I knew where I was. I just couldn't remember what I felt moments ago. And then all of a sudden, I'd remember exactly what I felt. I was feeling these sensations in the womb as an adult. I can only imagine the nightmare for the helpless tiny fetus. No wonder, the brain's thalamus has to block signals from the brainstem. We mustn't remember. G-d forbid. The neural connection transmission must not be permitted; otherwise, we might die.

My birth wasn't even remotely like natural childbirth in which case the baby tells the mother he or she is ready to be delivered, and the two work as one in loving harmony. An unwanted pregnancy leaves untold destruction in its wake, and handicaps the person for the rest of his natural life. If the person does not relive his horror in deep regressive feelings, he is condemned to a life of searching for love. He doesn't recognize his princess, even when the love of his life passes right in front of him, or if he is married to her, his eyes gaze and search elsewhere. He is still looking for his mother's love. If he remains neurotic, he will die neurotic, trying impossibly to obtain a love that should have been his, but never belonged to him. He had so much love to offer. He had the need to give his love. His mother had no such need. She rejected him.

"My mother had no such need." It took me almost sixty-six years to internalize these words, to accept them for what they really meant. Not the myth, not the fairytale that I desperately wanted to believe, but the hard cold facts. As Janov states, the unwanted neurotic is bound to be unfaithful in his relationships. I have found that the not wanted feeling is the most difficult of all to overcome. There is so much fear of not being wanted and so much need to be wanted. Present situations bring these feelings up all the time. Despite the ramifications of functioning in society, the betting odds in Vegas for me to lead a normal life would definitely be against me. However, this doesn't mean I should have been sacrificed to the wolves. I am trying to make a difference in this world.

The anesthesia came like one of my bipolar hallucinations. It relaxed all my muscles. I felt like a human guinea pig in my neuro-anatomy laboratory, cut open and beyond repair. Even my mother was losing her grip, as she was struggling to keep her grasp on me. The anesthesia did not have a pleasant aroma. The odor was familiar. I had broken my arm wrestling another kid in camp in the summer of 1950. At the infirmary, the nurse had taken a cloth or washcloth, soaked in ether and/or chloroform, to put me under, so the doctor could set my broken arm in a plaster cast. I therefore knew the anesthesia in the birth canal. It was the identical smell. General anesthesia in 1941 was not sophisticated like it is today, but it worked, crude as it was.

As the anesthesia set in, I was both relaxed and panicky, almost simultaneously. I didn't know whether I was going to make it on time, a panicky nightmare I live out in diverse ways in my dreams, and in the present.

I thought I heard a voice, and then I once again felt the touchless mobile energy lifting me upwards. I gathered strength, opened my eyes towards the shadowy light, and slithered on my own, like a snake, to the entrance of the womb. I remember touching the hole of the asp on my way out. I don't remember doctors pulling me out, but I do remember one last feeble try by my mother to keep me in. She was hanging on to my right foot, which soon broke free.

The next thing I remember was looking up at an overhanging light, while lying on a cold metal table. I gave a faint cry, but the nurses and doctors were incredulously staring at me. I felt ugly and shriveled up, tiny, helpless, and vulnerable, and only wanted to be held and comforted. Was this why I had struggled to survive? The doctors and nurses had abandoned me, and went over to my mother's bed. They were laughing and clapping.

My mother was to demonstrate her true colors. A kind nurse picked me up and covered me, and rocked me like the gentle rocking I momentarily experienced in the false Garden of Eden. I often reflect that, perhaps she was an angel, because I could still feel that same Divine energy in the hospital birth room that I had discovered in the womb. She took me over to my foul-speaking mother, who raised her hand and said, "Take that ugly baby away from me." The message was clear. The stares of the doctors and nurses were for an unwanted baby. And everyone in that room knew it. It's a scar that I still carry. It's the fear, anger, and rejection of not being wanted. I felt even uglier than I looked, and the experience branded me as inferior for so many years of my existence.

I was gently put down in some type of crib, but I now also knew that this person who carried me in the womb, and the person who rejected me in the birth room, were one and the same. The stinky smells coming out of her vagina, and her body odor in the birth room were identical.

I lived in fear each time they brought me to her hospital bed, and thereafter, throughout breastfeeding, and throughout child-hood, and most of my adult life. Still, the neurotic need inside of me still wanted her, needed her, desperately. I could never ever have her. I shouldn't say ever. Over the last couple of years when I visited her in the nursing home, we have sat together, hand in hand, for an hour, and she has just smiled at me. There were no words spoken between us, as we established a bond that I had sought exhaustively for so long. I honestly felt she was really seeing me for the first time.

I was still servicing her needs; however, it seemed I had cleared my soul and emotions enough, to where I could allow the love for my mother into my guarded heart. I tried to look beyond her roughness, crudeness, and aggressiveness, and for the first time, I saw the contentment that I was providing her beneath her exterior toughness. This strong independent lady had finally become a vulnerable old woman.

I think about these nursing home scenes often, and I ask myself in wonder. How could this be my mother? My mother was neither warm nor sensitive. Actually, neither of my parents really knew me; however, these times of clasping hands were sadly, the longest and best times I've ever spent with my mother. Amazingly, I cannot actually remember any other quality time with her when I've actually had her attention for more than a minute. A moment of praise from her was like winning the lottery. Pity for both of us. It's all gone. It's all lost. Never to be recovered.

I'm glad I returned to the womb to hear those awful words from my mother. They explain a lot about how I've felt all these sad years: ugly and inferior and easily embarrassed. It may be hard to understand how I could remember those words, but that's what she said when I connected to the exact energy of that moment in the birth room. Those ghastly words, "Get that ugly baby away from me," were stored in my brain until now, until I unlocked the vault that has kept them secretly hidden for sixty-six years.

The events, which I described, happened, and they can't be changed. However, I have helped to change myself, by returning to the past and feeling my pain. I now accept that it was what it was, and I am more kind and compassionate and not so hard on myself. I love myself for who I am with all my faults. My mother didn't need what I needed. She only needed herself, and certainly not a child to cramp her lifestyle. My father was a victim of his own neurosis, from his father and mother, and couldn't love me. He didn't get what he needed, and he expected me to give it to him, without him giving it to me. Dad never paid attention to me, nor did he praise me. His love wasn't real healthy love.

I'm grateful to my parents, and I'm grateful for who I am and for my life. My gratefulness has allowed forgiveness to creep into my life.

# 7

## MIRACLES

*B*Y THE FALL OF 1982, Yinnon had filled up seven research laboratory notebooks with his handwriting, each book consisting of three hundred pages. There was a lot of repetition, and he seemed to have reached a plateau in terms of making further progress. In an unusual display of frustration, he brought the seven notebooks to the edge of our Poquott loft, and proceeded to throw all of them in one thrust onto the floor below. He said he felt like Moses smashing the first set of Tablets, on which the Ten Commandments were inscribed. The sounds of the books crashing were silenced by a loud and strong male voice, that was definitely external. He heard the words very clearly, *"And you shall be Mine."* He remembers being both very startled and afraid, because he neither knew whose voice this was, nor could he figure out how the voice got into our cottage. There was no bipolar disorder or manic depression in 1982, so he couldn't blame it on mental illness. He heard the voice again, about two weeks later. This time the words were slightly different. *"And you shall have."* Could this be the Voice of G-d? I thought so ten years later, when Yinnon told me he revealed this mysterious occurrence to his Christian therapist, who believed him without a shadow of a doubt. We both went on with our lives but the voice never left him. Why did this happen? Yinnon had no explanation. Nor did I. He kept the notebooks, recording his primal feelings, for many additional years, before angrily dumping them in the garbage along with his Primal Therapy textbooks. He was to discover twenty-five years later that he would need these books again when he returned to face his demonic maker, his mother, once again in the womb.

Yinnon had been saved by miracles in the womb during an abortion attempt, which took his twin brother's life. One night I was wide awake in my bed, reflecting upon Yinnon's prenatal experiences. I felt myself gliding upward, levitating, under the control of an untouchable force of energy that totally surrounded me. I was in a completely non-meditative overtly conscious state, and I could not have been accessing my unconscious. I found myself being carried upward while suspended as if I were floating in water. I thought of Yinnon's description of himself as a fetus in the amniotic sac. As I traveled upward, my eyes gazed upon a passing solid shape that came into view. I clearly saw segmented stones, similar to what Yinnon and I had visualized in the Western Wall, on our Israeli bus tour the day after the Six-Day War. However, it wasn't 1967. It was the tail end of 2006, and this stone wall was under water. My levitation gently came to a halt. I could feel stares. It seemed like I was being examined by a group of formless *creatures* and a man with a full beard, who was definitely in charge. Were these the stares of angels who had abducted me, like the stories you hear about Martians or UFOs? The formless creatures were pensively swaying from side to side. They seemed to be in deep thought, trying to come to a decision. "Could this be the one?" I still have the head man's face in my memory. I can see him vividly in my mind. "Was this a man?" I thought. "Was this the transcendental G-d?" I was then lowered back down onto my mattress. It was all over in a matter of minutes. I remain perplexed.

In 1991, Yinnon had his first bipolar disorder episode. He became manic, and then he went into clinical depression. He was hospitalized at eastern Long Island's mental health Greenport facility and received electroconvulsive or electroshock treatments. The next few years were touch and go. In late 1994, he had a second major breakdown of agitated clinical depression, which caused further hospitalizations, and finally forced him to take a five-year long-term leave of absence from Stony Brook University. He had always maintained that the worst part of being in a psychiatric ward was when the door locked you inside and there was no exit to the outside world. His freedom had been taken away from him. His greatest fear as a child about being locked up forever in 999 Queen Street, the insane asylum in Toronto, had symbolically come true a half-century later. He was now a card carrying member of the mentally ill, and at the time, he thought that his destiny had been sealed for the remainder of his life. There would be no return to so-called *normal* life.

It was during his five-year hiatus from work that he and I both experienced miracles, which I wrote about and published in a book. It was also in March of 1995 when his agitated depression became unbearable, and he attempted suicide. He was almost successful, but once again was saved by Divine Providence. A few minutes more without help, and his life would have been over. Help came from volunteer firemen, who rushed him to the hospital. It also came from G-d Who implanted a supernatural message in my brain, for me to return home. I was forty-five minutes away and had just ordered lunch in a village diner when an extrasensory perception from an unknown source revealed to me that something was terribly wrong with Yinnon. I found him lying in bed, drifting off peacefully to greet death and his Maker. He seemed content, and he appeared calmer than he had been for a very long time. I was reluctant to wake him from his groggy slumber, but I couldn't let him go and be without him. The thought of losing him was unbearable; and besides, it wasn't his time. I jarred him and called 911. The fire department responded, and the doctors in the hospital saved his life on that cold day. It would take another six months of agony for Yinnon to get better. This almost certain death episode was followed by a much milder suicide attempt and further psychiatric hospitalizations. The depression lifted as suddenly as it came. Medication had no role in his recovery. Was it Divine Intervention? Was G-d once again there to help Yinnon? I think yes. If yes, why? Why so much help from the Creator?

The miraculous events that transpired beginning at the end of 1998 changed our lives and brought complete wellness, thank G-d, to Yinnon. There would be no more bipolar episodes. Yinnon had recovered and went back to work in September of 2000, and we began to make plans to retire. We set a time frame of five years. During the Christmas break of 1998, we drove down to Miami Beach, and parked ourselves at the Fountainbleau Hotel. It was a beautiful sunny day in South Florida. The clouds there are wonderfully unique. They are so magnificently angelic white and puffy when set against a powder-blue sky.

We were lying on our lounge chairs, when Yinnon abruptly halted our conversation and pointed heavenwards. What we saw was perhaps the most incredible sight I have ever seen. Pictures of Yinnon as a little boy, a teenager, a young adult, and then an old adult, were flashing in the sky in very rapid succession, just seconds apart. Quite remarkable was the fact that these heavenly photos were the very same ones, which Yinnon had stored away in his picture albums. I knew this to be true, because he often showed me these unhappy pictures. There were one or two photographs of himself as a cute, blonde, curly-haired smiling little boy that he loved, and was forever trying to recapture within himself. Unfortunately, the identical photos in both his albums, and in the sky, showed him, as he put it, as ugly and neurotic, with tightness and tension lines in his unhappy face. It was only by luck and a phony smile that he was able to pose for any kind of camera picture that he could live with. One of the main reasons he told me that he had entered Primal Therapy was because he couldn't smile.

Yinnon had started to lose his already thin hair in his early thirties and amazingly this loss of hair was depicted in the sky. From mild loss to the full hair loss horseshoe pattern, we clearly visualized it all directly above as heavenly flashes. Not only did we see him at his present age, but also he was being given an extraordinary glimpse of himself into the future. There were several repeated remarkable flashings of him well into old age. The remaining hair on both sides of his bald scalp appeared almost wildly Einsteinium as he aged. Yinnon wore a hairpiece, but G-d saw and loved him in his natural state; there was no hairpiece in the sky. After the slide show ended, we were both numb with wonder. It seemed as if G-d was telling us that Yinnon would live a long life. But what about me?

All of our miracles became the catalyst for our biblical self-study. We wanted to divorce ourselves from our past, refine our character, and embark on a new spiritual road. We had a thirst to seek a higher purpose. We immersed ourselves in the Hebrew Bible, G-d, Evolution and Creation, human anthropology, and a host of other subjects. We read voraciously, waking up in the wee hours of the night and then discussing everything in inquisitive back-and-forth, one on one, Talmudic fashion. We tried unsuccessfully to come up with reasons for free will and the existence of humankind with its good and evil inseparability. We became each other's conscience, and continued well into the night until we became so exhausted that our brainwaves stopped recording. There was no division between us, and we became one person and not two. It was during this period that each of us developed new spiritual thoughts about our purpose on this earth and in the World to Come.

During our vacation in Florida, we saw a beautiful white egret, with an enchanting slender neck, fly directly past the front of our car. Moments later, we saw cloud-like white letters in the light-blue sky, spelling out the name of Yinnon's son Sean with the *S* capitalized, followed by the *ean* in lowercase letters. Within a fraction of a second, the *an* became *th*, now spelling out his identical twin brother's name, Seth. We were dazzled. Our eyes remained glued to the sky. We saw Yinnon's sons' names, Sean and Seth, rapidly alternating for a full ten to fifteen seconds. Immediately after this, we saw blurred writing in the sky. The first capital letter, *M*, was absolutely clear, as were the small letters, *ia*, at the end of the word. However, we couldn't make out the middle of the word, no matter how hard we tried straining our eyes. It all happened so fast. When the heavenly visions had disappeared, we started to think about the blurred word, and we realized that, perhaps the answer could be found in the initials of the first names of family members. Yinnon's wife's name, Marcia, began with *M* and ended in *ia*. But we also had the letter *M* from his eldest daughter, Melanie, and his son-in-law Magnus. We were being sent a message in the clouds, and the word was blurred, because there are four family members whose names begin with the letter *M*. Only Marcia's name fit with the *ia* at the end of the blurred word. The pieces of the puzzle were beginning to fit together.

Yinnon had believed that the naming of his five children had been random. Marcia was his wife from a second marriage, and his biological children were Melanie, Seth and Sean. His non-biological children were Erin Michelle and Kenneth Scott. Kenny had married

Karen Michelle, and the two grandchildren were named Sarah and Ethan. In a remarkable insight, he realized that the first letters of the given names of his children and grandchildren corresponded to the first four letters, "MESS" of the word Messiah. He could fill in the "IA" of Messiah from the ending ia of the blurred word in the sky. The final "H," he could find in his granddaughter's name Sarah. Was this a coincidence, or was this Divine Providence? Yinnon and his family seemed to be in some way connected to the Messiah. But how?

In my case, the drama of miraculous events was significantly less evident. Yinnon's experiences were nothing short of heavenly. Of the two of us, I was more determined to climb the spiritual ladder, and I have done so for the past ten years. A thought came into my head, from out of the blue, that I should start a nonprofit charitable corporation for the Third Temple, which would be essential to the coming Messianic Age. The Third Temple was the Creator's promised dwelling place on earth. It was where His *Shechinah* is prophesied to reside at the End of Days, as it did in the Tents of the Patriarchs, the Tabernacle in the Sinai Desert, and in the First Temple centuries ago. I gained nonprofit status by successfully obtaining a 501 (c) (3) classification for the Shechinah Third Temple, Inc.

Yinnon and I were not practicing religious orthodox Jews. We thought of ourselves as personal spiritualists. However, our steadfast beliefs in the Messianic Age, and the Third Temple, made us orthodox in our hearts. As we continued our studies, we found a theoretical answer to what we thought was our mission. In the biblical commentary to the Book of Isaiah, we learned that there would be two Messiahs. One from the Tribe of Joseph, Messiah ben Yoseph, who would die in battle and be resurrected forty years later by the second Messiah, Messiah ben Yehudah, from the Tribe of Judah. We also discovered that before the world was created by G-d, He knew

the name of the Messiah. Imagine our surprise, when we learned that Yinnon was one of the names of the Messiah, proposed by many of the wise Jewish sages over the past centuries. It all seemed to fit and it was surreal. A figment of our growing imaginations, perhaps? We had a hypothesis, but how were we to prove our theory? Could I really be the Messiah ben Yoseph, and could Yinnon be the Messiah ben Yehudah? Ridiculous? Our souls were on fire. We threw caution to the wind. We believed in the grandiose, yet we were not manic. Or were we?

# 8

# LETTERS TO THE REBBE

*THE CHABAD LUBAVITCH* movement was started, as its own Hasidic group, by Rebbe Schneur Zalman, the Alter Rebbe. In the eighteenth and nineteenth centuries, many of these Hasidic groups sprung up and flourished in Eastern Europe and Russia. By the end of Second World War, most of these groups had disappeared. Yet, the Chabad group continued as a movement, thanks in part to the vision of the recently deceased seventh Lubavitch Rebbe, Menachem Mendel Schneerson, who died in 1994. Yinnon and I probably would have remained ignorant of Chabad had I not become friendly with Rabbi Adam, the Stony Brook University Lubavitch rabbi. Adam and I both share the same vision of a Messiah and Third Temple at the End of Days. One hot summer day in the new millennium when we were sitting outside my office at the Dental School, I was expressing to Rabbi Adam that I was at a loss to know how to proceed with the Third Temple. I had secured the necessary Internal Revenue Service nonprofit status, but now what? I had also written more than a hundred, mostly Jewish, foundations for start-up funds and sent letters to just about every Jewish celebrity, as well as others, asking for donations. In addition, we applied via the legal route for a trademark patent, and we also wrote about the Shechinah Third Temple and the Messianic Age on our Third Temple Web site. Adam suggested coming back to his house to write the Rebbe. He saw that I had a puzzled look on my face, because the Rebbe was dead.

Adam explained that Rebbe Schneerson had asked his followers to publish all of his important letters that he had written over the many years to individuals who had written him for advice and help. The letters were written in both Yiddish and Hebrew, and they were published as a set of thirty books. Adam had all the volumes back at his house. He said that I should write a letter to the Rebbe, insert it into one of the thirty volumes, and then we would read the Rebbe's letter, and see if there was any connection to my letter. It sounded bizarre; however, after the experiences Yinnon and I had, nothing in life seemed to be out of bounds.

We drove back to the Stony Brook Chabad house. Once inside, Adam put *Tefillin* on me, and we said a prayer. He then gave me a pen and a blank sheet of paper and then instructed me to write my precious letter to the Rebbe. I wasn't prepared. I scribbled the following:

*"Rebbe, I want to know my role in the pursuit of the Third Temple. I believe G-d will once again bring the Temple site to Bethel. Does G-d need my humble help to pursue a Temple for the Jewish people? Should I continue my fundraising efforts and educational efforts ideas, and keep working toward the goals of the Third Temple? Or shall I stop?*

*I love G-d with all my soul and wish only to serve Him. But it is difficult to do it all alone. I know He is with me. I just need guidance on how to proceed. I'm afraid I did not write this well."*

Rabbi Adam asked me which of the thirty volumes I wanted to place my letter in. I didn't hesitate and chose number ten, biblically symbolic of the Ten Commandments. I closed my eyes and stuck my hastily written folded letter between random pages in Rebbe Schneerson's tenth published book volume. Adam first read my letter then turned to the Rebbe's letter, which he told me was written in Yiddish. Adam flipped the pages back and forth many times, between my letter and the Rebbe's, and I hadn't a clue as to what was happening. Finally, he looked up and said, "The Rebbe has answered you." I realized then and there that there was a purpose for the Rebbe to have these letters published and also that my coming here today was destined. Adam confided that he, too, wrote the Rebbe, whenever he needed advice in his spiritual pursuits. Adam typed out an English translation account of the Rebbe's letter, which was dated in 1953, and had been mailed to someone in Europe or Eastern Europe.

*"The Rebbe received a letter from someone, who is undertaking a project that he fears will create a lot of changes in his life, and therefore, he is asking from the Rebbe a blessing in order to carry the project through and to expand the existing project.*

*The Rebbe responds noting that G-d has always given the strength and potential to individuals in order for them to carry out their life's mission.*

The Rebbe further writes.

*It is most fitting to point out the saying of our wise sages that 'G-d Almighty did not create one worthless thing in his world, and thus automatically it is given to each and every one of us, the strength and potential to carry out and fulfill his mission and his purpose in this world.' An increase in strength and potential is commensurate to the purpose. Since the mission that is placed upon each and everyone of us is within the realm of holiness, it is permissible and possible to expand upon it. As the sages have said, 'All that add, they add to Him.' For when a person takes it upon himself an added mission, this in and of itself increases the pipeline through which will be drawn to him strength and potential from Above.*

*G-d willing, he should also decide to increase his Divine service, and his efforts in strengthening Judaism, and in general, the spreading of the endearment of the Torah and Mitzvahs, and specifically, (the spreading of) Chassidic philosophy, its traditions, its ways, and its foundations. For, in the end, this is what he is cut out for: his main specific purpose. And automatically, he will expand and strengthen his holy Divine service and his importance in this service and in his general endeavors."*

It was kind of incredible that the Rebbe's letter to a stranger in 1953, applied to me. The Third Temple was to be part of my mission in life. I was to advance the Divine by spreading His spiritualism, and by learning about the grandeur of Chassidism, and praising its righteousness. I have indeed taken steps to learn about the Chabad by studying the basic religious tenants of Chassidic philosophy, as outlined in brilliant clarity by the Rebbe Schneur Zalman in his five-volume masterpiece, *Lessons in Tanya*. I left the Chabad house and Rabbi Adam with renewed vigor. I felt I would succeed somewhere down the road. I certainly didn't have even a smidgeon of the noble character of the Patriarch Abraham, who had undertaken his second mission to have the world recognize One G-d. I don't mean in any way to compare myself to this glorious, kind man. However, I do have sincerity in my heart and soul, and I would do anything for my Creator. Little did I know that I was about to be tested on my spiritual convictions.

# 9

# MY BLUE HEAVEN

*I*T *WAS TIME ONCE MORE* for Yinnon and I to try his time line therapy. The Moses regression had become a wonderful memory for me, and we were curious to see if that mystical experience, twenty-five years ago, was just a fluke. We picked a warm winter night with the moon casting its pale glow, and parked the car at the deserted parking lot of our Valencia Lakes clubhouse in Boynton Beach. It was midnight, and it was a magnificent night. The sky resonated with an unusual royal blue tone, and was filled with an abundance of brightly lit stars that seemed within a ladder's reach.

As we sank deeper and deeper into our meditative state, releasing the heaviness from our bodies, I could feel all of the mental tension and physical pain evacuating my musculature. No sounds would tempt me from my reverie; we had transgressed our respective zones of bodily noise to enter the realm of silence. All movement now became involuntary, as our brains had yielded, and surrendered control of our bodies. Another force, a primeval force of calm, was directing us now. That force of energy carried us gently out of the car, levitating us in an unconscious state. We had lost all communication with ourselves, as we floated in free suspension, higher and higher.

An unknown amount of time had elapsed, and where we found ourselves next was a total surprise. We had landed, in an erect stance, on the border of a lawn of solid greenery lined with magnificent shrubbery every color imaginable of all earth's flowers, and even some exotic florals that we had never seen before. The aromas of their perfumes in the air were irresistibly sensual, and my unremarkable penis felt like it was in perpetual orgasm. Plants and trees filled with all sorts of mouthwatering vegetables and fruits dotted the grounds. Most unusual were the trees with their magnificent multicolored leaves, which, if you rubbed them anywhere on yourself, could lift your spirits and bring healing to your body, mind, and soul. I picked a yellow plum the size of a tennis ball from one of the plum trees, and I was in heaven with my first bite. The sweetness of the fruit was exquisite; it reminded me of the yellow plums I had eaten by the bagful when we were in Israel completing our doctoral degrees. There seemed to be no end to this Garden of Eden. As we glided on air over rolling hills, we passed inviting bubbling hot springs and the gentle ripples of quiet flowing streams. The sky was powder blue, adorned by the same pristine, puffy white clouds that we loved in the Florida sky. The sun was a brilliant orange-yellow, and remarkably, my eyes weren't bothered when I gazed directly into its center. I was feeling outright delicious, and my entire being was immersed in this glorious setting.

The perimeter of our *Shangri-La* could easily have enclosed an area of 1 and 1/8 square miles. The surroundings were so vivaciously different from anything we had ever visualized before, making us question whether we had regressed to a past life. We were mesmerized by the appetizingly, picturesque beauty of the place. We wondered, "How could we be so high up, and yet the temperature be so warm, so perfect?" If you have ever been on an airplane, you know that the outside air temperature is very cold when you ascend to the high altitudes of the clouds. I had my compass with me, and we started walking in a north westerly direction. In the distance, we spotted what appeared to be about a twenty-story apartment building, but this structure was radiantly glowing, as if it were made of gold. As we approached, we saw rose-colored stone walls and Lebanon cedar gates enclosing this golden architecture. When we arrived at the Eastern Gate of the structure, a man with a short and stout appearance looked down from the platform and greeted us. He spoke in English, telling us that he was the gatekeeper, and that we had been expected. When we asked where we were and why were we here, this impish little fellow just snickered and directed us inside. Little did we know that he was the well-known prophet, Elijah, in disguise. Elijah had been taken by G-d while he was still alive, and according to the Hebrew Bible, he was to return to earth prior to the official beginning of the Messianic Age. We ascended twelve steps and passed through two one-hundred-foot tall gold plated, cedar wooden doors, with even larger palm crowned pillars extending on each side of the hall entranceway. I immediately recognized where we were, and quickly realized that our feet were standing on the marble tiles of the Outer Courtyard of the Third Temple. That meant that our luscious sensuous Garden of Eden, which we had just delightfully strolled through, was the Temple Mount. The size of the Holy edifice was more in line with Ezekiel's Temple measurements. The whole structure approximated 1/8 mile on each side, and was barely longer in the east-west direction as compared to the north-south direction.

I was familiar with the structure of the Third Temple and its dimensions, because I had read the description in the Hebrew Bible's Book of Ezekiel. The prophet Ezekiel had been transported from Babylon to Jerusalem during the Jewish Babylonian exile, almost

2,500 years ago, and was shown an elaborately detailed *Merkavah* (mystical) vision of the Third Temple by G-d. I had also read Rabbi Steinberg's and Chaim Clorfene's elegant, explanatory, diagrammatic texts on the Messianic Temple, so that there was no doubt now where we were. The Outer Courtyard was where the Jews gathered back in ancient times during the First and Second Temples to pray to and honor G-d with their sacrifices. I whispered to Yinnon that his time line therapy had propelled us into the future. "We were," I told him, "in the future Third Temple." "Not possible," said Yinnon. And we each turned out to be correct. Yes, this was the Third Temple, so I was right. However, we were to learn that this Third Temple was the heavenly counterpart to the future earthly Third Temple, which would exist at the End of Days.

Kabbalah sages have long ago strongly stated that it was indeed from the Heavenly Temple, G-d's Throne of Glory on High, that the Creator fashioned the Light of Creation. Before the Big Bang could take place, there had to be a conversion of nothing to something. This is the uncertain period in time, prior to the Big Bang, which physicists cannot explain. In these stark moments before Creation, there was a primeval darkness without space or time. All was nothing, and from nothing, G-d fashioned a limitless infinite energy, known as the *Ein Sof* Light, so that our lower world as we know it, and the higher heavenly worlds of angels and souls, could emanate from Him. The spiritual Big Bang, according to the Kabbalists, was the clothing of the *Ein Sof* Light by means of a series of numerous "energy contractions" (*tzimtzumim*). One of the first contractions stemming from G-d's Light was Divine Intellect to the uppermost world of *Atzilut.* It is reserved for the unique souls of our three Patriarchs (Abraham, Isaac, and Jacob) and also for special souls like Moses. ChaBaD is an acronym of Divine Intellect for *Chochma* (wisdom), *Binah* (understanding), and *Daat* (knowledge).

My mind was racing at lightning speed. I had read the biblical Jewish controversy on whether we humans would build the Temple, or whether the Third Temple would descend from heaven? The intermediary consensus, which I favored, was that man would build G-d's footstool, the Third Temple's physical structure because it is one of our 613 Commandments, while G-d would provide the *Shechinah*, His Divine Presence. The first view was popularized by Rabbi Maimonides, an outstanding religious Jewish scholar and sage who lived in Spain in the thirteenth century, and by several other prominent Jewish sages. Their opinion is based upon G-d telling the Israelites in the Sinai wilderness to build Him a Tabernacle, so that He would dwell among the Jewish people. Rashi, Chaim Luzatto, and other sages were proponents of the Third Temple in Heaven descending to Israel. Their arguments like those of Maimonides were based upon biblical verses. The intermediary view seems to be upheld by history, and was true for both the Tabernacle in the Sinai desert during the Exodus, and in King David's and King Solomon's First Temple.

I now found myself leaning toward the second theory. Why build a magnificent Third Temple? G-d can simply duplicate and transport the architecture of the already existing heavenly spiritual-physical structure to earth at the End of Days. It would certainly make it a lot easier. The costs alone of the Temple with its gold-plated holy structure would be in the billions. As much as I thought that this would be the easier route to avoid all the hassles and infighting among us mortals, once we got down to the brass tacks of actually deciding to build the Temple, something didn't sit right with me. G-d has repeatedly created spiritual-physical Covenants with man since the time of Adam and Eve. A new bold Covenant can only hold if both parties, G-d and human beings, participate equally in the Third Temple. One could easily argue against the intermediary position that the Covenant would still be fulfilled if an exact copy of the Third Temple descended from heaven.

Well, we knew where we were, but we didn't know why we were here and why we were expected? At the gate to the Inner Courtyard, we were greeted by a man who introduced himself as Michael, the chief archangel. Michael was tall and handsome and had a commanding presence and stature. He looked just like us, but we had learned from our biblical readings that, when necessary to tone down fear, angels can transform themselves into humans. Abraham, Jacob, Daniel, and Ezekiel had all encountered angels in human form.

Michael told us that he would be our advocate during the interview process. We were dumbfounded. In a quiet, gentle, respectful voice, I asked, "What interview process?" Michael smiled, and warmly responded, "The *Moshiach* Interviews, of course. You are being interviewed to be the Messiah." "Both of us?" I responded.

Michael looked me straight in the eyes, and as gently as he could to shock me out of my stupor, he said. "Yoseph, you can no longer fool yourself, deceive yourself, into believing that your twin Yinnon has been with you all this time. He was lost a long time ago in your mother's womb. Yinnon was the tragic victim of the abortion. You, Yoseph, or correctly Yossel, are the neurotic in Primal Therapy that survived so many times by G-d's Hand. You, Yoseph are the bipolar. You, Yoseph are the only scientist professor at Stony Brook University, now professor emeritus. Yinnon sadly does not exist, although he once did. You, Yoseph are the one, who indeed had the Moses Time Line Therapy. However, it was your friend Howie, who led you through the regression that evening in your Stony Brook office. Your bus trip after the Six-Day War in 1967 was with your first wife. When you returned to Israel and climbed Mount Sinai, that was in 1983 on your honeymoon with your second wife, Marcia. Marcia is your *bashert*, your soul mate, that G-d has sent you to give you joy in the midst of your suffering. She has stood by you always, and with G-d's help and

her extrasensory perception, Marcia is the one who saved you from
dying in your suicide attempt in March of 1995. You, Yoseph, and not
Yinnon, are the father of the five children—Kenneth, Melanie, Seth,
Sean, and Erin. And you are the one whom G-d has chosen to bestow
all His miracles on, ever since He visited you in your mother's womb.
It was G-d's Voice that spoke to you alone in your Poquott cottage,
"And you shall be Mine." When those formless creatures, my angelic
colleagues, you describe, levitated you and brought you before G-d as
a fetus, it was with a singular purpose, and that purpose begins now.
To see if you can be the Hebrew *Moshiach* or *Mashiach*, the Messiah
for humankind?"

"We have deliberately chosen a sinner: you, Yoseph, who has
knowingly cheated in science. Yet, you have publicly repented and
confessed your sins to your Stony Brook University administra-
tion, and sent letters of apology to the former institutions that you
attended. Moreover, you have expressed your heartfelt remorse and
your sincere regrets for all of your sinful actions in your published
book, *Divinely Inspired: Spiritual Awakening of a Soul*, for all to see.
We have intentionally selected someone who has suffered horrifically,
yet has the potential through his suffering to look inside and understand human nature. We also have especially not chosen a *tzaddik*,
the wisest, most righteous, and perfect of men. We are testing the
potential of a simple imperfect man. If you succeed in answering
our questions, you will become King Messiah, and return to earth
to take your place at the End of Days. Hopefully, you will respond
well. If our assessment of you is that you are not the person, we had
hoped you might be, then we will have failed once again in finding
the true Messiah. Do you want to now continue Yoseph, and enter
the gate into the Inner Courtyard? If not, you can still turn back,
and all of this will be erased from your memory. You can go back to

your life as it was, with Yinnon as your dead companion. No hard feelings as they say in human speech. Your choice, but I must have your answer in the next five minutes. The others are waiting. Ask any questions you wish?"

It was all a dream, or so I thought. I was psychotic, and was having my delusions of grandeur. The Temple Mount and the Third Temple were a hallucination playing tricks on my mind. I began to feel the old paranoia creep back into the recesses of my brain. I was not in heaven. I was really at 999 Queen Street, the insane asylum, and I was never getting out. I was manic and psychotic. I was the Messiah of the loonies. My poor lost twin Yinnon had been my scapegoat. As long as Yinnon was by my side, I was not alone and didn't have to face my inner demons. The Primal Pain became Yinnon's burden and suffering, not mine.

For the five-minute allotted period, I could not get any words out of my mouth. All of the alone and unwanted feelings of Primal Therapy returned. Yinnon would always be in my heart, but I was now alone to face my Maker. I had survived the unbeatable foe in the womb, and once again I was feeling like the tiny helpless fetus. Yet this time, it seemed that I was playing high-stakes poker with a hand that I surely could not win. I needed a royal flush, but the chances of that were one in a billion.

Yes, I was intelligent, but how could I respond to such heavenly giants of superior knowledge? I wasn't an orthodox Jew, nor was I learned in Talmud or Kabbalah. I had some Torah under my belt, but it was sparse and self-taught, and I was just beginning to gain a little bit of wisdom and confidence. "Why would G-d choose a spiritually-inept, morally-challenged human being like me? Surely, there were better choices."

I felt like the ants I used to stomp out as a kid. I was nothing, miniscule, a speck of dust. I wanted to run as fast as I could back to the safety of the womb. However, I laughed silently at that choice, for obvious reasons. The panic escalated. Terror invaded. I felt a huge burst of anxiety in the pit of my abdomen. There was no one to consult. There never was a mommy or daddy to help. There was no one here to turn to. It was all up to me. If I chose to stay, I was on my own. Yet, if I stayed and was successful, I would finally be special and feel wanted. I would be crowned as king, and anointed the Messiah. "No," I said out loud. I have to do this for the right reasons. I have to do this not for myself. It was the greatest challenge of my life, and I tried to convince myself that this is what I wanted. I finally knew my mission in life. Wow! I was as close to G-d as I thought I possibly would ever get. I was at the Pearly Gates. No matter what happened, I felt it was win-win. Even if I didn't become the Messiah, I could not lose.

The quote from *Julius Caesar* came into my mind. My wise boss, Izzy, in the Oral Biology Department at Stony Brook often quoted Shakespearian lines to me. I had spent the last six years with him discussing everything from politics and military strategy to spirituality, but Izzy wasn't with me now. It was my call.

> *"There is a tide in the affairs of men,*
> *When taken at the flood, leads to fortune;*
> *Omitted, all the voyages of their life*
> *Is bound in shallows and in miseries.*
> *On such a full sea are we now afloat,*
> *And we must take the current when it serves,*
> *Or lose our ventures."*

The *Macbeth* quotes also swamped my brain again, and I felt a yellow streak down my back.

*"The attempt and not the deed confounds us."*
*"Cowards die many times before their death;*
*The valiant never taste of death but once."*

Despairingly for just a split second, I reflected on a quote of a biblical commentator that applied with terrifying accuracy to my mother and me. I was the seed that had emerged from her womb, but would I germinate to my full potential in life?

*"If the field is barren,*
*The seed, howsoever, potent*
*Will not germinate."*

My mother was a barren spiritual field. My last thought, before I made my decision was a quote sent to me from Raj, with whom I had wanted to do holistic research while I was working at the university:

*"Faith is the bird that feels the light*
*And sings when the dawn is still dark."*

Michael was patiently waiting. He smiled when he looked straight into my eyes. "We have your answer," he joyfully exclaimed. "Now follow me, Yoseph. And good luck." We climbed eight steps and entered the Eastern Gate between the Outer and Inner Courtyards. As soon as we were inside, the sounds of voices and music greeted us. The Levite priests were singing and playing their tunes from King David's Psalms. They were standing on a five-step choir platform, which they referred to as the *Duchan*. The Inner Courtyard was about 200 square feet, and was surrounded on all of its sides by the Outer Courtyard. I was surprised to note that the *Duchan* stretched across much of the area of the Inner Courtyard. The musicians played their tunes on lyres, flutes, lutes, trumpets and cymbals. The sounds of their music were like a prelude to a symphony. The musicians wore white silk shirts and silk balloon pants and sandals. The singers also wore identical clothes and shoes, but their color was a sky blue. I started to gleefully hum their songs.

As we marched past the Levite Priests, we entered the Priestly Court of the Inner Courtyard. I immediately recognized the familiar sacrificial altar with its sloping ramp. So this is where all the Israelite sin offerings were presented before G-d! I pictured the slaughtered sheep, bulls, goats, cows, and birds being burned, and I became nauseated. I have always believed such sacrifices to be pagan, and felt that I would probably not survive the interview process, because of my biased opinions.

I marched on to my fated destiny. It was too late to turn back. I had made a commitment, and after my almost successful suicide attempts, I had vowed to never give up on myself again. I prayed for the Creator to be with me, to help me. I prayed that I would make Him proud. My entire life passed in front of me. All of the good and bad memories were then gone in a flash. Yesterday was left behind. Another day had dawned.

# TODAY

# 10

# GABRIEL

*STRAIGHT IN FRONT OF US* was the House of G-d. This House or Fortress, as it was called, was the twenty-story apartment building that Yinnon and I had seen in the distance as we walked along the grounds of the Temple Mount. Closer inspection revealed that the Holy Temple was on ground level while the rest of the building was hollow, ascending some 150 feet. Michael, heaven and earth's chief archangel, and I climbed the eight steps from the Inner Courtyard and passed through the Hall (*Ulam* in Hebrew) leading into the Sanctuary (*Heichal* in Hebrew). My eyes immediately searched for the three golden landmarks of this Holy chamber: the Menorah, the Showbread Table, and the Incense Altar.

The Sanctuary was about forty feet wide in the northerly-southern direction and eighty feet in the east-west direction, and the whole House was sloped on a mountain, which was Mount Moriah's earth equivalent in heaven. My eyes easily adjusted to the brightness of the room. There was no evidence of electricity anywhere, and I was in awe of the possibility that the entire space of this holy chamber was lit up by a golden six-foot Menorah bearing just seven eternal burning oil lamps.

All was silent, and the air was filled with the aroma of spices from the Incense Altar. In front of the Altar was a semicircular table with seven chairs. Michael instructed me to sit facing the table, and then he sat down beside me. I felt like the accused at a murder trial, except that there was no judge or jury in sight. I marked time with a golden silence in this Holy room, where the walls were gold-plated covering cedar wood layered over stone. The cedar panels were etched with palm trees and cherubim angels, so that there was a palm tree between every two cherubim. Each cherub's head had two faces, a human face and a lion's face that shared scalp hair and faced in opposite directions. The artist's patterns were strikingly visible through the hammered-on gold plating.

The silence was broken by the sounds of wings as a formless creature flew into the room. He took on a defined form as he sat in the center chair facing me. I knew him well. His appearance gave him away. *"He was clothed in linen, his loins girded with fine gold; his body like the precious blue stone, Tarshish, his face like the appearance of lightning, his eyes like flaming torches, his arms and legs like the surface of burnished copper, and the sound of his words like the sound of a multitude."*

Oh yes! I recognized this man as the angel Gabriel from my readings of the Book of Daniel. In this book, I see that Gabriel's presence caused Daniel's joints to shudder, his strength to waiver, and all color to leave his face. Daniel fell to the ground in complete horror until Gabriel switched to the guise of a man.

When I saw Gabriel, I was trembling involuntarily, but I managed to keep my composure. Realizing that I was at a disadvantage, Michael, my advocate, requested that Gabriel become human as he had centuries ago with the righteous Daniel. Gabriel begrudgingly complied, although there was still the sound of his voice, which sent streams of cold shivers flowing down my back. His physique took on the appearance of a body builder who had returned from a Caribbean vacation. His skin was not just tanned; it became copper tone in color.

Gabriel was clearly annoyed. His first question to me was set in defiance. He was daring me to answer. He looked behind him, beyond the Showbread Table, the Menorah, and the Incense Altar to the curtain and doors leading to an even Holier chamber than the Sanctuary we now sat in.

*Gabriel:* (Pointing angrily) Do you know what's behind the curtain?

*Yoseph:* Yes. The Holy of Holies.

*Gabriel:* Well, this simple human has a tongue. Son of man, continue.

I knew that he was trying hard to bait me into making mistakes, because then he could get rid of me. Angels had never been overjoyed when G-d made the decision to offer His Torah to humans. At the time of the splitting of the Sea of Reeds, the angels had questioned whether the Israelites were any different in moral character to the pursuing Egyptians. He had a valid point.

I tried to ignore his egging me on. I responded as he had commanded.

*Yoseph:* The golden Ark of the Testimony, containing the Two Tablets of the Ten Commandments, sits on the Foundation Stone, the *Even Shtetiyah*, in the Holy of Holies. The Ark itself hosts two cherubs on its golden lid surface. The cherubs' faces are childlike, male and female, and they are half human and half birds with wings. They sit on each end of the lid of the Ark and have one eye toward each other in conjugal devotion and the other eye looking downward through the Ark to the Tablets of the Ten Commandments.

Impatient and irritable, Gabriel changed the subject to throw my concentration off.

*Gabriel:* Who am I? Name three places in the Hebrew Bible where I have been?

*Yoseph:* Why, you're the Angel of Fire, and your powers operate both in times of peace and on the battlefield. When the Assyrians lumbered at the gates of Jerusalem after killing and then exiling survivors of the ten Northern Tribes (the Lost Tribes), it was you who boldly, in one fell swoop, destroyed their entire army. Your powers are beyond human imagination.

Then, when Ezekiel was transported from Babylon to Jerusalem by G-d in a *Merkavah* (mystical chariot) vision of the future Third Temple in Israel, it was you Gabriel, with your six-cubit (approximately twelve feet) linen cord, who proceeded to take the measurements for the Temple.

I was just about to speak of Gabriel's encounters with Daniel as my third example when he rudely interrupted me as if he had read my mind and knew exactly what I was going to say.

*Gabriel:* No, I don't want to hear about my time with the righteous Daniel and his dreams of the End of Days. You shall respond to this topic at a later time in the interview process. I want you to now tell me what a miracle within a miracle is. Remember, son of man, you have no margin for error. One mistake and we will turf you out. This is not a driver's license test in which you can make mistakes and then still pass, like you barely did in Toronto. Your score must be 100/100.

How did he know about my driver's license? I was twenty when I took my test, and I had thirty-six points against me. The limit was forty points, and I almost failed. Gabriel was correct. I felt his impatience and responded smugly.

*Yoseph:* The parting of the Sea of Reeds during the Israelite Exodus from Egypt. That was a miracle in which G-d used His omnipotent powers to cause natural forces to divide the waters. This is an example of a miracle within a miracle, because the waters of the sea rose up and miraculously flowed upward on both sides of the division to create the land bypass in between. Water always naturally flows downward. G-d had interfered with the Laws of Nature. Divine Providence was at work.

*Gabriel:* I won't be like you, son of man, with the smug smile. I won't gloat. Yes, you are correct. However, you didn't give me a proper third example. Where was I directly involved in a miracle within a miracle?

I immediately realized that I had fallen for his trap. I had been too arrogant with my smug smile. This was not a game of usurping a great angel and servant of G-d. I had failed. Tears welled up in my eyes, for it was obvious that all was lost. The interview process would terminate before it got underway. Then lo and behold, a surprise change in Gabriel's personality.

For the first time during the interview process, Gabriel, who was all business when it came to doing G-d's business, showed compassion. He then spoke gently:

*Gabriel:* To be a Messiah, the highest job on earth, there must be no arrogance within you. All must be humility in your heart and soul. Do you understand? (I nodded.) Now, can you provide me with your third example?

I responded with all the sincerity in my heart and soul, out of reverence for the Creator. I had been given a second chance.

*Yoseph:* The example I am about to recite is not directly from the Hebrew Bible. I do remember reading a *Midrash* commentary about Daniel's three young wise friends, Chananyah, Mishael, and Azaryah. They had been exiled with Daniel to Babylon at the time of destruction of the First Temple, some 2,500 years ago, by Nebuchadnezzar, king of Babylon. The king had raped the gold and silver of the Temple and constructed an obelisk idol as a tribute to himself. All were required to bow down to the king's statue. The friends had considered how to proceed, because bowing to a statue was idol worship, and above all, an act of blasphemy that would not be tolerated by G-d. They went to the prophet Ezekiel, but when they asked him for advice as to what to do, Ezekiel did not answer them directly. He urged them to avoid a direct confrontation and go into hiding until the situation blew over. When they disagreed, Ezekiel said that he would consult G-d. Ezekiel returned and told the three friends that G-d could not, would not, help them. The young boys were not dismayed, and they replied that they would offer their lives for the sanctification of His Name. The boys found salvation, and that's where the miracle within a miracle comes in.

Chananyah, Mishael, and Azaryah were thrown into a fiery pit. Yurakami, the Angel of Snow, came forward and told G-d that he would go down into the pit, cool the fire, and save the boys. Before G-d could give his approval, you, Gabriel, stepped in and spoke. If Yurakami cools the fire, that would be a miracle. However, if Gabriel, the Angel of Fire, cools the fire with his own fire, that will be a miracle within a miracle. And so it was. G-d yielded to Gabriel's plan. Shortly thereafter, a mighty wind blew the statue down.

*Gabriel:* You seem to have a grasp, son of man, but do you know the significance of the story?

*Yoseph:* I can only offer personal suggestions. I do this with humility, as my opinions should be taken lightly. The significance of the story of the three boys and King Nebuchadnezzar isn't only written in the Bible to awaken our pure Jewishness, our *pintele yid*, which will be needed to bring the ultimate redemption of the Messiah and the Third Temple at the End of Days. There is far more relevance to the story.

It is incumbent upon us to not only be good Jews and righteous human beings who support Israel, but we also need to finally line up behind G-d no matter the cost to our personal material world. G-d has graciously given all of us life, whether we choose to believe it or not. We should be willing to stand up and be counted at times when we might have to sacrifice our material goods and/or forfeit our own lives. Many of the Jews who were slaughtered by the Nazis during the Holocaust did not have the means to leave their homes or were immobilized in helpless shock and disbelief. However, for those who could flee, many did not want to give up their material possessions. Berlin had become their Jerusalem.

Daniel's three friends' actions justify the miracles of the Exodus from Egypt. G-d has invested in us by kindly and mercifully selecting us as His first grandchild among the nations. We have to ask ourselves if we have fulfilled our end of the bargain, when we can't even adhere to and follow His Ten Commandments.

*Gabriel:* I find your response to be only a partial explanation. You haven't satisfactorily answered why the Almighty created miracles in ancient days and now in modern times, with only a few selected and privileged humans like yourself. You need to expand more upon your reasoning.

*Yoseph:* I can only give you my humble opinion. As the anthropologist Ian Tattersall stated, "Human beings, despite their unique associative mental abilities, are incapable of thoroughly envisioning entities that truly lie outside their own experience or realities that cannot be predicted from what they have known in the material world." For many people, Tattersall's insight brings forth the human logistic case against One Omnipotent, Omniscient, Omnipresent G-d, because G-d seems to not be part of our present everyday world.

In biblical times, miracles provided the Israelites with vivid experiences of clarity that removed any doubts about belief in G-d. My miraculous experiences did the very same for me. I find it difficult to comprehend why the great majority of Jews living today do not believe or have faith in G-d. However, I recognize that it's not easy to abandon your intellect in favor of faith in a Supreme Being, with whom you have no contact.

My connection to the three boys' story with Nebuchadnezzar, I believe, is that I too must find a way to give back to G-d so that I also will be able to justify the miracles of the Exodus and the giving of the Torah and the Ten Commandments at Mount Sinai. G-d has bestowed upon me so many gifts, for which I am grateful.

*Gabriel:* Can you elaborate further on the relationship of miracles to the World to Come and why there aren't more Jews who believe in G-d, given their ancestry and history? You alluded to this earlier; however, you gave no clear answer.

*Yoseph:* When you say "the World to Come," I think you mean the Messianic Age. I believe that all of the miracles in this world are a preparation for the next world at the End of Days. This current world is imperfect, but we are marching on to a more perfect world. Nobody knows the time frame, but it seems to me that you must first experience imperfection before you can truly feel comfortable with perfection. If this world were like the imaginary TV show in the movie *Pleasantville,* where all good things happened, then it would be impossible to move on to the more perfect *Shangri-la* in the World to Come. It's kind of like knowing hate in order to truly feel love at its deepest level or experiencing poverty to really understand and appreciate wealth.

With regard to Jewish belief in G-d, I am at a loss to explain why surveys indicate that only 30 percent of Jews actually believe in G-d. The percentages are so much higher in both the Christian and Muslim faiths. The irony is that you find many of the disbelievers sitting around the Passover Seder table year after year, enthusiastically retelling the ancient story of the Exodus of the Israelites from Egypt. You even find these same disbelievers attending synagogue, although the percentage of Jews at religious services, relative to the rest of the Jewish population, would be considered as surprisingly small.

Although one would think that Jewish ancestry, culture, and history would naturally promote monotheism, these facets of the religion may be precisely the reasons why Jews don't believe. Religion's promise of salvation unintentionally locks horns with its perceived rigidity and loss of freedom. For many, the orderly path of religion actually is an impediment to freely float our spiritual souls. In addition, I would contend that secular Jews often hedge their bets and are agnostics rather than atheists. The old expression, "There are no atheists in foxholes," comes to mind.

As I read recently in a newspaper article, it may be that celebrating the richness of the tradition at Passover or going to religious services on the High Holidays is enough for some. G-d isn't a necessity in their everyday lives. Perhaps because of upbringing, others may simply choose not to believe altogether. Ironically, G-d has given us free will, and we turn that against Him by not believing in Him. There are also those who, in Star Wars' terms, have chosen the dark side.

Or possibly, the answer may lie in Judaism being a religion of laws and customs rather than a religion of faith and/ or miracles, like Christianity or Islam. I tend to favor an explanation to your question by highlighting the hidden *pintele yid*. In each Jewish soul, belief in the Creator already exists from conception or birth. The *pintele yid* is the innermost core, the purest point, of your Divine Soul. However, this point is purposely hidden by G-d, awaiting discovery and exposition. The Jew himself, not G-d, has to ignite the spark. I kind of like the *pintele yid* theory, because it involves personal spiritual growth and applies to all human beings. Moreover, those Jews who are attracted to Buddhism may be actually accelerating their unearthing of their Divine Souls, despite a lack of belief or need for a Creator in the Buddhist religion. You get your feet wet pretty fast with Buddhism. Judaism is a struggle because it is not experiential unless, like miraculously for me, the Creator chooses to intervene in your life or you possess unshakable, steadfast faith from the beginning, like my wife Marcia.

From my perspective, connection to G-d may only require a one-way conversation with Him. He may not answer you in words, but my faith tells me that He will answer you nevertheless. I'm not referring to prayer. A personal verbal chat may be enough to yield unanticipated results.

I can appreciate the reluctance to looking to the heavens and speaking out loud to the thin air. In all of us, there is always another force in our brains that negates our decision to move forward, especially if it means embarking on a road to G-d. I'm sorry, Gabriel, that I have no definite answer to your question.

*Gabriel:* You've answered well enough, but I've heard it all before. There have been others, with wisdom far greater than yours, who have come before this tribunal and uttered your exact words. Now tell me, do you see anything wrong with your human testimony thus far? Furthermore, you have not spoken about all of this from G-d's viewpoint.

I panicked. I was stumped. I didn't expect these statements from this masterfully diverse and wise angel. My human testimony? What did the angel mean? Then I thought about the word "human" and realized what Gabriel was hinting at.

*Yoseph:* Yes, Oh G-d, there is something I may have been doing inadvertently without realizing it. Much of what I have been speaking about is about me. The Messianic Age is not about the Messiah. It's about the coming of the age of G-d, when there will be miracles that will go far beyond the Exodus and Sinai, and will be incredible even to the Creator. As the Messiah, my purpose is to serve Him and His children. I'm ready to do this.

I saw Gabriel's first smile. Nothing else of anything that I said had moved him. He probably had heard it all, centuries before, with other interviewees seeking to be the Messiah.

As to Gabriel's second statement, I realized that I had omitted an important part of why Jews may not believe. I began by telling the angel that one problem is that Jews may be knowledgeable, or not, of their Jewish history, but they may fail to recognize a pattern that G-d seems to display with regard to the survival of humankind. I elaborated with humility.

*Yoseph:* I don't pretend to understand G-d's essence; however, it seems to me that G-d desires, for whatever reason, to ensure survival of the earth and humanity until we enter the more perfect world of the Messianic Age.

It is not religion that offers salvation to humankind. It's the World to Come, the Messianic Age—that is, if we are lucky to be a part of it. The expiration of Cain's lineage, the Flood and Noah's Ark, the Tower of Babel, the destruction of Sodom, the promise of the Land of Israel to the descendants of Abraham, Isaac, and Jacob, the miracles of the Exodus from Egypt and the declaration of the Ten Commandments and the Torah at Mount Sinai, the conquest of the idol-worshipping Canaanite nations by Joshua followed centuries later by King David, the exile of the Jewish people after the destruction of the First and Second Temples—all were stepping stones, and even prerequisites, to ensure survival of humanity. Even all the bloodshed of history cannot stamp out G-d's plan. Neither past wars nor present day Islamic Jihad can destroy the earth, no matter how hard they try to do just that. G-d will step in, as He always has.

G-d created the world *ex nihilo*, out of nothing. With Adam and Eve, He became the G-d of both heaven and earth. As time passed, people turned away from the Almighty, taking Him for granted or turning to the stars or human-animal idols for worship. It was time for action, so a new order for civilization had to be established. At the presentation of the

Ten Commandments, there was a leveling of the playing field so that good now had an equal chance to stand alongside evil. The only game in town, in that populated region of the world, were the Jews. Only a group of humans with a potential to uncover their *pintele yid* were worthy in G-d's Eyes. There were no organized movements of Christianity or Islam 3,300 years ago, so it all fell upon the Jews, for better or for worse. The Egyptians and Canaanite nations were idol worshippers, and G-d already knew that they would never give up their lifestyle to receive His Torah. He had looked into their hearts and understood their nature. The Jews were G-d's first grandchild. Christians and Muslims were supposed to be the second and third grandchildren, although such a statement is hotly disputed among religious groups.

When His Divine Presence departed from the First Temple, just before the Temple was destroyed, the Creator was disappointed. The Jews, as a force of divinity in the world, had dropped the ball they were chosen to carry for humankind. With the Second Temple predestined to also be destroyed, G-d made a conscious decision, I believe, to be the G-d of heaven only. That didn't mean He gave up His stewardship of the world. However, He did get off the public stage more than two thousand years ago, and He faded into the background, leaving man to deal with the path that man had chosen. The Covenant between G-d and the Jews had been broken, and it was up to the Jews, and not G-d, to restore it. The sages speak about G-d leading man in the direction man wishes to go. Despite man's screw-ups and his inhumanity to man, G-d is still with us watching over His world to ensure its survival, until we can walk together into the Messianic Age. With the world set on its own destructive course, it seems there is a rocky road ahead, perhaps with an apocalyptic ending in store as a prelude to our Messianic symphony.

Many people, of all faiths, have spoken about how we get to the Messianic Age before we self-destruct. My feeling is that we might do it through the duplication of this heavenly Third Temple on earth. The truth is that none of us know, except G-d, what will bring us to a new world, a rekindled Garden of Eden.

*Gabriel:* I see the way your mind works. Let's test the truth of your emotions. Can you be honest, Yoseph, and tell me whether you have any reservations about being the Messiah? You are the first person actually seeking the job. All others interviewed thus far have not. Why pick someone who wants the job? "Greatness doesn't develop from someone who seeks greatness. It evolves from someone who doesn't desire it but is called upon."

I felt embarrassed by his remark, and there was anger brewing inside of me. Why is this angel such a hard ass? Does my wanting to be the Creator's Messiah make me an egoist and, thus, disqualify me. Yet, I had to admit, there was truth to his inference. Yes, I do have doubts. Not that I don't think I would do a good job. In reverse logic, it actually may be better to have someone who passionately seeks the position.

I realized that my own words had just trapped me and Gabriel knew it, too. I had no choice but to be honest. I answered.

*Yoseph:* I just don't know about living the kind of life that I imagine being the Messiah will entail. It will be very different from my current lifestyle in Florida. Human beings, as we know them, will be different. The inclination to do evil, the *yetzer hara* in Hebrew, will disappear, or at least be muted, and prophesy will return to our children. There would have to be a conversion of the human brain to a higher evolutionary level—not necessarily intellectual, but at the very least, emotional.

And then a stunner from the angel of fire.

*Gabriel:* You may want to be the Messiah, but from what you have just said, I'm wondering if you have *kalut hanefesh*.

I thought to myself: What was *kalut hanefesh*? Why doesn't he just speak English? I looked into Gabriel's deep fiery eyes and realized that I was on my own. My mind raced with anxiety. I calmed myself and then recalled one of the Hebrew words for soul: *nefesh*. I had seen this term before, but where? When I was at the Weizmann Institute for my doctoral degree, I unfortunately only learned a few scattered words of Hebrew. Then it came to me. I had seen the term in my reading of the Alter Rebbe, Schneur Zalman's *Lessons in Tanya*.

"Kalut hanefesh—*a consuming passion of the soul.*"

I had spoken the truth to Gabriel. I did not have that burning passion to be the Messiah.

Regrettably, I realized that my desire to be the Messiah was, yes, to give back to my Creator, but also I was driven by my neurotic ego—the need to feel special, have something of my own. I was the one in Primal Therapy. Yinnon had died during the abortion. My pre-birth and afterbirth had been one continuous nightmare. I never felt special to my parents, never owned the moment, in fact, any moment of love. As a consequence of not feeling I belonged to them and they to me, I was driven neurotically to search elsewhere in life to find something unique that I could call my own. It was a hopeless journey in the present. I was seeking the wind in the field, trying desperately to retrieve a parental love long gone and irretrievable.

Sadly, even the unforgettable blessings I received from the Creator could not fill the empty hole in my soul. I find that mind boggling and unacceptable. I feel disgusted with myself. Gabriel had vanquished the vampire within me and had driven his stake directly through my heart. Strangely, it felt good to admit that I would not be the righteous saint I anticipated I might become. I would remain as imperfect as everyone else. All I had going for me was that the non-neurotic part of me loved G-d with my heart and soul. In spite of my shortcomings, I still wanted to reach for the stars. I still wanted to be the Messiah, provided I could help G-d achieve his lofty goals for humankind.

Gabriel smiled once more. He had extracted my cancerous secret. He spoke softly:

*Gabriel:* There is much more to come in the interview process. I take my leave. May G-d be with you, Yoseph.

Without another word, Gabriel switched into his angelic form and disappeared as he had appeared. I was sorry to see him go. The softness of his last words to me had touched my soul. Unlike Jacob, who wrestled with the angel of his twin brother, Esau, and won, I had lost my battle with Gabriel.

*Michael:* Gabriel doesn't give out compliments, although he did smile twice, which is quite rare. You are still here, Yoseph. Consider this an honor. We move on. Let's go back outside to the Temple Mount for a walk and some delicious fruit. You've done well, Yoseph.

I've done well? I wasn't sure of Michael's optimism. I felt insecure with my response to those last questions but happy with the outcome. Gabriel was the toughest of interviewers. I didn't think he particularly liked dealing with the imperfections of human beings,

but there was an unexpected soft side to him, which I cherish to this day.

*Yoseph:* Thank you, Michael. Without you, I couldn't do this.

*Michael:* You're welcome, Yoseph. Try to dismiss your enlightened interview with Gabriel from your mind. You will need all of your being and strength for the task ahead.

How could I wash this great angel's majestic words away? The interview was already marked indelibly in my brain.

# 11

# THE SEVEN SHEPHERDS

*WHEN MICHAEL AND I* returned to the Sanctuary, seven distinguished men sat around the semicircular table. All sported beards, except for the youthful-looking man occupying the center chair. I had no idea who these inquisitors were, until Michael introduced King David, the chairperson of the group. Then I knew exactly who they were: the seven resurrected shepherds who will accompany the Messiah at the End of Days.

On King David's right sat Seth, Chanoch, and Methuselah. Seth was Adam and Eve's third son, from whom all of mankind descended after their eldest son, Cain, killed his younger brother, Abel, and the genetic lineage of Cain was allowed to run its course and eventually die out. The Third Temple would be erected on earth at the End of Days to rectify Cain's sin of murder, and perhaps all senseless murder, present and past.

Chanoch was the father of Methuselah, and he lived 365 years compared to his son, who was the oldest recorded person on earth, surviving 969 years. Chanoch walked with G-d and was taken alive by Him before he lived out his allotted years.

King David, sitting at the center of the table, had survived a mere seventy years. He was wearing a plain, gold, six-pointed Star of David around his neck. To his left sat the greatest prophet of all, Moses, who had died at age 120 and was forbidden by G-d to cross over the Jordan into the Promised Land. On his left wrist, Moses wore a gold, double-chained bracelet, symbolically attached on each end to miniature tablets inscribed with the Ten Commandments.

Adjacent to Moses was Jacob, who was the son of Isaac and the grandson of Abraham. Jacob had four wives, who gave birth to twelve sons and a daughter. The sons became the Twelve Tribes of the nation of Israel. They would unify to build the Jewish nation, and their descendants would stand with Moses at Mount Sinai to receive the Ten Commandments and G-d's Torah. Jacob died at age 147, and through his son Joseph, viceroy of Egypt, Jacob spent the last seventeen years of his life as the world's first retiree.

Jacob was wearing four rings, two on each hand, perhaps for each one of his wives. Three of the rings were made of gold, and his left pinky ring sported a sparkling emerald while his wedding ring finger had a diamond chip and two dark-blue, glowing sapphire stones geometrically balanced on either side. The right pinky ring shined of platinum, and a large star sapphire covered the ring's entire top surface. There also was a unique diagrammatic inscription on both sides of the star sapphire stone, almost akin to steps leading up to a diamond sacrificial altar. The adjacent finger displayed the third gold ring. The ring's head revealed the luster of onyx with an embedded diamond triangle and a raised brilliant ruby stone kept in place by four gold prongs.

At the end of the cherry wood table sat Abraham, who represents the figurehead of the earth's three monotheistic religions. Abraham had lived healthily to 175 years of age. He is suggested to be the first

Kabbalist, and he wore the red string, symbolic of Jacob's beloved wife, Rachel, on his left wrist. Rachel's energy of protection against negativity is said to lie within the red string. On Abraham's right wrist was a simple looped gold and diamond chipped bracelet.

King David was the first to speak. He spoke in musical notes, as if his words were being sung. He had written the Book of Psalms, the songs of which he recorded on his lyre or harp. It is said that you must understand the workings of his harp in order to solve the riddles of the psalms. King David would arise at midnight, awakened by his harp, which began playing on its own when the breeze of the Jerusalem night air plucked its strings. The more King David strummed his harp, the more intense and harmonious it sounded. Simultaneously, the more he plucked his Divine Soul, the more he ascended the spiritual ladder to G-d.

King David instructed me on the ground rules of the interviews. Each of the Princes would question me on a variety of topics and could mix and match their queries depending on my responses. I was awestruck by the company I was privileged to be in and felt that I didn't deserve to be here. I felt tiny in relation to these great men.

Gabriel had been as tough as nails. These figures of men, at first glance, seemed to be a little gentler, but I was under no illusion that these princely interviews wouldn't be just as difficult.

We were about to start when I asked respectfully if I could use the bathroom. My anxiety levels suddenly skyrocketed, and my stomach was churning with those worms again from my neurosis and bipolar disorder. I needed to get to the bathroom quickly before I embarrassed myself.

# 12

# METHUSELAH

*T*HE OLDEST MAN ON earth. How incredible to be facing him.
He certainly didn't look his 969 years; he looked as if he could
have been my maternal grandfather. He was gentle as a lamb, and I
was hoping that Methuselah was the same. Momentarily, my mind
drifted to a saying from a Chinese fortune cookie that was taped onto
my university office window for many years. It said:

*"Your soul is worth all the riches in the world."*

I said a silent prayer and hoped that my soul would be up to the
task ahead.

*Methuselah:* Good afternoon. My first question to you,
Yoseph, is why are you here? You are clearly out of your league.
I am not referring to myself, because I am just a tired old man,
but look at the company you are keeping at this gathering.

I thought I was back in the womb again. My startled reaction, where
all went wrong beginning in the first trimester of my mother's pregnancy.
The chills of fear down my back had returned, and I was shivering as

if I had the flu. My heart started to beat irregularly, and I felt terrified that my visible anxiety would surely trip my atrial tachycardia. If my heart began beating two to three hundred times a minute, as it had on past occasions, I knew my goose was cooked.

Methuselah, sensing my despair, read my emotions, and assured me that my heart would be fine. Another mind reader like the angel Gabriel? Did they all have special powers in heaven? If they did, I reasoned that I had better not lie, because there was an invisible lie detector attached to me.

An uncharacteristic smile appeared on my face. I thought of the words to a familiar song, "This old man, he plays one. He plays knick-knack on my thumb. With a knickknack, paddy whack, give your dog a bone. This old man came rolling home." I guess I should have expected what was to happen next, but I didn't. The old man sitting in front of me, with the gentle blue eyes, was whistling my tune, beaming that I was singing a song about him. Methuselah seemed to have all the patience in the world, especially compared to *moi*, who had adopted his mother's lifelong impatience.

Whatever confidence I had going into these interviews had been shattered by Methuselah's first question. I was caught off guard, which was to be typical for me in these Messiah Interviews. Indeed, he was absolutely correct. Who am I among these giants of men? I was just a *pisher,* as they say in Yiddish. Was this interview a competition to flush out my inferior skills?

My response was honest.

*Yoseph:* You're right Methuselah. I don't belong here. Maybe it's better that we stop now, before I make a fool of myself. I can't compete with men who have been judged by such high standards in their time. I really don't have anything new or unique to offer.

*Methuselah:* We didn't bring you all the way to heaven for you to cop out. When the going gets tough, the tough doesn't get going. Life is not about hiding from the fray, it's about being immersed in the heat of the battle. That's when a person rises to great heights. Life is about the tests, which each of us face. G-d purposely places these challenges in our path so we might improve our character and be successful. Sure, some of us get more suffering than we would like, but G-d doesn't give us more than we can handle, providing we have faith in Him and we behave righteously.

You have to take punches, get knocked down, and then get up again. That's what the biblical words, *"The righteous shall fall and rise seven times,"* signify. Look, Yoseph, the Almighty has given you more than your share of help. He recognized that your life has not been a bowl of cherries. There are humans, too numerous to count, who have had it far worse than you. You are not here to feel sorry for yourself. You can do that on earth, but not in heaven. This interview is taking place for the most cherished job a spiritual human being could ever desire. It's for all the marbles, as you moderns would say. The closeness you will have to your Creator will be unimaginable and unparalleled—perhaps even greater than G-d's love for His servant Moses.

The old man was right. I was feeling sorry for myself—the "poor me" syndrome. It wasn't that I was not grateful for my life. I was. I truly was. G-d had entered my life with Divine Providence and had changed me for eternity. I was not bitter about my upbringing. I was thankful that I had the parents that G-d gave me. They hadn't changed, and that was okay. I was the one that had improved my character during my lifetime, and my spiritual soul grew stronger with each passing day. A wonderful quote from a biblical commentator came into my thoughts.

> *"G-d offers His fragrance to all, but His wine is reserved for those who are righteous and wish to be guided by Him."*

I began my reply.

*Yoseph:* About ten years ago, when my family's names appeared in the sky, and I subsequently made the secret connection to the acronym, Messiah, I thought that this was the telltale sign from the Creator to indicate my mission in life. I believed with all my heart that G-d was telling me I would have a role in the Messianic Age, although He never ever mentioned my being the Messiah. Being the Messiah is a figment of my imagination, my passion, and my neurosis. As I told Gabriel, I might not have the passion to be the Messiah. However, I have reached a point in my life where I see G-d in everything I do, think, touch, smell, taste, hear, and see. I am able to perceive G-d in the shadows, in good times and in bad. My faith, similar to my wife Marcia, has become unshakable.

For the longest time, I have been yearning for G-d's miracles to continue to infuse my being. I now seem to have settled in feeling quite comfortable after ten years of spiritual searching. My success at Primal Therapy, in truth, was not enough, and from my friend Yvette, I have learned to bring G-d into my life as my partner. Whenever life becomes overwhelming, or just difficult, I pray to G-d and ask that He take on my burden. And it always seems to work.

I have climbed the spiritual ladder by separating my Divine Soul from my physical material being. Yet, I still need to let go of more of my physical burdens and call on G-d to take over when my vigorous efforts fail. G-d has never disappointed me. He has always come through. My Kabbalah name is, "Forget thyself." My problem for years was taking on all of the burdens by myself, without drawing from the Garden of Eden's Tree of Life. All this has changed, as I have become a spiritual human being and can now line up behind G-d. I feel that I finally belong to G-d, as He had asserted forcefully in 1982 in my Poquott cottage, when I heard His Voice say, *"And you shall be Mine."*

Our Creator seems to choose individuals with troubled pasts. However, each of us in this room has probably sinned, with the exception of the archangel, Michael, sitting beside me. That's how G-d created human beings, and that's the main reason the human race has survived. G-d in His infinite wisdom and mercy realized that we humans are but flesh. Having a troubled past, and being asked to take on a leadership role, humbles you. Cleansing the past through repentance of your sins doesn't eliminate the memory of those sins. The spiritual road requires much more than your deeds. It necessitates investment of your time and energy, and the higher your personal desire to ascend, the more you stumble. Yet, ironically, the more you stumble, the easier it is to get up again.

I can't realistically match the deeds of the elite individuals at this table. Yet greatness is born from your inherent potential, and only G-d recognizes that in you. You may feel that you control your own destiny. However, it was G-d who gave you your talents, and it will be G-d who will determine whether you indeed achieve greatness. Many intelligent people have the G-d-given talent to be the Messiah, but without G-d's permission and assistance, it will never happen.

G-d saw it in Seth, as all mankind descended on the right track compared to his evil brother Cain's descendants' wrong track. He has yet to reveal what Chanoch's role will be in our world and the next. And in your own case, your wonderful longevity gives us so much insight into our present world's medical ills.

G-d has looked into the hearts of Abraham, Jacob, King David, and Moses, and saw His diamonds in the rough. Each one had to tap into their potential and grow into leaders. G-d knew that they had the goods, but they had to discover and grow their spirituality by themselves while forging a Covenant with the Creator. With G-d's faith and trust in me, I think I can rise to my potential. In the end, G-d will determine whether I will be the Messiah, based, of course, upon recommendations of this group to Him.

Timing is everything, and the time is ripe for the Messianic Age. We are at the pinnacle of our technological advancement, although improvements will always be forthcoming. We also may not be far from human destruction of our world. The next evolution will come with the last frontier of science: the brain. There would have to be major changes in the brain if man's evil inclination were to be subdued. Man, as we know him today, is likely to become extinct, as have virtually all past species. I happen to be the one, among all of us, living in these dangerous times, so maybe sheer familiarity with the modern world is one of the reasons I am being interviewed.

Individuals will still possess their free will in Messianic times, although it seems to me that, with an evil inclination subdued or eliminated, being King Messiah of Israel might be more a figurehead role to bring people together in peaceful times. It is our human nature to squabble, even in the absence of wars. The chosen Messiah must not only be as wise as Solomon. He also must be a dreamer and lover of fantasy. The next world will be incredibly wondrous, as children shall prophesy with a new level of imagination. Physical healing and physical purity of our contaminated environment will take place, and food will be plentiful enough, to the extent where poverty will be eliminated. Humans will have food, clothing, and shelter. G-d will perform miracles, incredible even to Him. There will be jobs for everyone, because we will be looking for answers to our problems from the spiritual and not physical world.

My experience in Primal Therapy has allowed me to truly understand the flawed nature of human beings. Moreover, throughout the ages, we have neglected a very important point. Nowhere in the Hebrew Bible is the role of the Messiah spelled out. It is true that the criteria for becoming the Messiah has been defined, at least, in the eyes of some sages, like Maimonides.

One possible role of the Messiah might be to assist G-d in determining who will make it to the wonders of the Messianic Age. In my estimate, not everyone will be selected to enter the Messianic Age.

*Chanoch:* I heard a lot of platitudes in your answer to Methuselah, but you didn't convince me that you are worthy of my support. You have no passion. Furthermore, why not just choose among battle-tested individuals like King David, Moses, Abraham, or Jacob, and make one of them the Messiah?

I expected a direct assault on my personage. However, I was surprised by the attacker. I felt victimized, as if I was a child again. Trying to temper my anger, I responded:

*Yoseph:* According to scriptures, the Messiah will be a descendant of only one of the Twelve Tribes of Israel, the Tribe of Judah. This dates back to Jacob's deathbed blessing of each of his twelve sons. Judah would be the one to bear the scepter and give rise to the royal family of Israel. The sole member of this illustrious panel, who is a member of the Tribe of Judah, is King David. It is very clear in the Bible that the Messiah will come only from David's lineage. That disqualifies Moses, who was a Levite, as well as both Jacob and Abraham, who preceded the division of the Jews into Twelve Tribes. That still leaves David, of course, and coincidentally he happens to be sitting alongside you at this table of Princes. David can defend himself. He doesn't need your help, Chanoch.

I detected what I thought was a sarcastic frown of disbelief from King David, as I erroneously reasoned that he and I were now competitors to be the Messiah. He interrupted.

*King David:* You have been disrespectful, Yoseph. We can tolerate annoyance, but you must be respectful to this tribunal. One more such angry outburst will disqualify you, and you will be sent packing. Do I make myself clear? Now answer Chanoch's question as best as you can.

I had been admonished—put in my place, and rightly so. I had crossed the line, belittled this fine man. I apologized sincerely to Chanoch and the group. I couldn't look at Michael sitting beside me, because disappointment in me and my inappropriate ire etched his brow.

I thought to myself, "What do I do now?" The thought of this question brought me right back to my panic-terror feeling in the womb.

I'm all alone, all by myself, without any help. Where do I turn to for help? There is no one to help. I feel so helpless and vulnerable.

I thought of Charleton Heston and his portrayal in the movie *Ben Hur*. A scene in the movie that touched me deeply was when Ben Hur, played by Heston, turns to see Jesus giving his charismatic Sermon on the Mount speech. There was this beautiful music playing, and it has always stuck with me and melted my soul.

It then came again. That same energy I had felt in my mother's womb, after she aborted my twin, Yinnon, but could not close the deal and kill me too. G-d had saved me in the womb during the abortion, and at birth, and I now felt His Divine Presence once more in this Holy Chamber. As I heard the *Ben Hur* music, glorious chills pervaded my body. My eyes welled up and tear droplets ran down my face. This was followed by a heavy stream, as I was visibly crying for all in the Sanctuary to see. I had once more been spiritually touched by the Hand of G-d. Michael handed me a soft tissue. I dried my wet, teary eyes and, for the first time in this interview process, spoke with conviction and passion from my heart. I led with my soul.

*Yoseph:* My less-than-humble but respectful answer to you, Chanoch, is that I would not be happy if King David was chosen over me to be the Messiah.

Surprisingly, nobody in the room was shocked by my assertiveness. King David's mouth had formed a smile. I continued.

*Yoseph:* My words to you are not just words. Anyone can spout words. My words are truths that come from the heart and my soul—words that I will apply into action. All my years in Primal Therapy have taught me how to feel and express my deepest of emotions. My spiritual growth, in turn, has instructed me in the ways of G-d, which are the ways of truth and honesty. Yes, I have had doubts, like all of us humans have. Anyone involved in moral growth slips and stumbles, and fails while he or she succeeds. Yet, at this very moment, I want to be your choice to be the Creator's Messiah.

The Israelites were at the height of their commitment to G-d when the Ten Commandments were given at Mount Sinai. That represented their true essence at that moment. The problem was that they could not sustain their elevated spirituality, and they floundered and lost their chance to be a kingdom of priests and a beacon of light to the rest of the world.

I pledge in front of all of you Princes and the chief archangel Michael in this Covenant, which I today make with the Almighty, that I will sustain my commitment to G-d. My scientific training as a researcher competing for grant funding, my broad life experiences, growing knowledge, and my total self-reliance has allowed me to see both the whole picture and all its details. I will know what to do. I have a G-d-centered vision for the Messianic Age.

G-d is in this chamber with us, and His *Shechinah*, His Divine Presence is inside all of you. I see that so clearly, as I gaze upon the glow emanating from each of you. I hope that His *Ein Sof*, His infinite Divine Light, will too shine on me. However, I still need to earn the glow, like all of you did, when you were alive on earth.

All of the interviewers before me began to clap, and then they spoke in unison:

*Interviewers:* We were wondering when your passion to fight for this position would surface.

I glanced at Michael sitting beside me. Angels don't clap, but Michael, too, was moving his hands, and miraculously normally silent energy was converted into sound. The moment could not have been more special. I felt honored.

*Moses:* Are we to be your judge and jury? After all, the Almighty has called upon us to interview you.

*Yoseph:* No. I hope you will be my advocates. I remember what G-d said to you at Mount Sinai when you were pleading for G-d's mercy for the Israelites. *"I, G-d, will have mercy and kindness on whomever I desire."* G-d is my ultimate judge and jury, as He was and is yours.

This afternoon in front of the Almighty's Holy of Holies, I have asked G-d to strike a new Covenant with me. G-d's Covenant with Abraham, Isaac, and Jacob that their descendants will be as numerous as the stars and will inherit the Holy Land still holds today. It is my belief that at the End of Days, whoever in this world is fortunate to enter the Messianic Age will be the descendants of the Patriarchs, Jewish or not. All that are good and sincere in their hearts will enter. My feeling is that G-d's edict includes those agnostics who are wavering in their belief in Him yet are nevertheless acting righteously in this world and following G-d's ways.

Those who are not true in their hearts will live out their lives on earth but will not enter the Garden of Eden. They will be subject to the random vicissitudes of everyday life. The latter embraces atheists of all sorts who scoff at the notion of a Supreme Being and who, through their oral or written words, try to convince others to follow their deceptive paths.

The world is G-d's Creation, and He has decided, in His Wisdom, that the Jewish people shall be the possessors of the Land of Israel. Keepers of the Land of Israel not only means occupying it, as we as Jews do today, but it also means lining up behind and belonging to G-d to truly make Israel Holy. My interpretation of *Holy* encompasses more than a religious belief. It also lies within the realm of humility and spirituality. Marcia's principle must be all-pervasive. "No one has the right to hurt you." Belonging to G-d means being compassionate and kind and merciful in your heart to those less fortunate than yourself. Holy implies following the Ten Commandments.

*King David:* Can you be more explicit?

*Yoseph:* I'll try. G-d offers unconditional love to the human race. This is His fragrance. If you want His wine, you have to earn it by living a meaningful spiritual life. A religious life can fulfill the requirements of a meaningful life, but so can the life of a person who loves material possessions. It all comes down to the sincerity of what's in a person's heart, in his true desire to help one's fellow. Orthodox Jews, whom I have great respect for, would argue that being a Jew depends upon following G-d's Will and the 613 Commandments. I have a different definition of what following G-d's Will implies.

King David said it in his Book of Psalms. *"G-d is good to all and His love extends over all His works."* The fragrance is His offer of goodness to all, but not all are His works because of the moral choices people make in their lives. Those that follow His lead, His works, receive His wine. It seems so simplistic. Yet, it is the only thing that makes sense to me. G-d knows that we are imperfect. That's how He created the human race. We each have a lifetime to justify to G-d, whether we should be permitted entrance to the Messianic Age and His Garden of Eden.

*King David:* I'm glad to see you are thinking out of the box. You'll need to think past the influence of ordinary men in order to be the Messiah. Your wisdom will have to be better than that of the wisest man, paralleling the heights reached by my son, King Solomon.

*Yoseph:* With the L-rd's help, I will gain the wisdom with each passing day. In this way, I will take my cue from Jacob, who prepared for war with Esau while praying to G-d, even after being assured by G-d that He would protect Jacob. G-d willing, I will try to be worthy of being called righteous. I will look to Jacob and never take my righteousness for granted.

I looked at Jacob, who now took my statements as his cue to insert himself into the interview process.

*Jacob:* I know by looking into your heart that you are sincere and are not trying to flatter me. However, I have to be blunt. When I examine your soul, I see that you have not achieved *tiferet,* or harmony and splendor. Your ego is still too large a part of you, and we cannot recommend you for the Messiah. I am sorry. You need to unanimously satisfy all seven of us, and there is much more of the interview ahead. In fairness, I will give you one chance to respond.

Why did he have to be so blunt? He wasn't nice. Won't any of these committee members give me a break? And I hadn't yet heard a peep from either Seth or Abraham. This was Methuselah's session, and each one of the interviewers would have their own session, with interjections by any of the seven.

I knew that Jacob could see right through me. He had boldly defeated Esau's angel in a wrestling match and had been rewarded with a second name, Israel, which also became the same name for the Land of Israel, granted to the Patriarchs. He had outfoxed Laban, by giving up twenty years of honorable minimum-wage service in the process of marrying two of Laban's daughters, Leah and Rachel, and their two handmaidens, Bilhah and Zilpah. Jacob was the chosen one to father the Jewish nation, and He had met G-d face to face in his dreams of a ladder to heaven. Jacob's face is said to live on, on G-d's Throne of Glory in heaven. In G-d's Eyes, Jacob never died.

The truth was that Jacob was right. I did have an ego because of my neurosis, although when I was just about to express this, I hesitated. Everything depended on my next answer, and somehow I felt that Jacob already knew this, and this was not the answer he wanted. I asked him for more time, which he agreed to.

Several minutes went by, as I thought deeply about my character. Who was I really? I realized that I did have a serious flaw that went beyond my privately hidden impatience and neurosis. Everyone needs an ego to make it through life in one piece. My flaw was that I lacked humility. I gave it my best shot, and presented the following discourse to *Jacob:*

*Yoseph:* Kind sir. You are correct. Part of ego is arrogance, and my lack of humility makes me arrogant in a subtle way, which I did not recognize until now. The Creator blessed me with intelligence, deep thinking, and now spirituality, and I lost sight of my humility to others who don't have these qualities. I was bored with conversations, even with friends, because I found the conversations not intelligent, deep, or spiritual enough. I am appreciative, and do have enormous gratitude for where I am in life, and for all of my life since its beginning in the womb. You can't, however, be the Messiah and govern the Jewish nation if you don't have humility. These same, quote, "boring" people might be able to do a better job than I, if they were given my talents.

Also, in my desire to be open and honest, I admit that I have prejudice to shed. I am not particularly crazy about some of the practitioners of the religion of Islam.

Adam and Eve were not punished by G-d for eating the forbidden fruit. G-d's was the first psychology lesson in human history on how to parent children. He was trying to teach Adam and Eve to be adults and act responsibly. G-d made Adam and Eve accountable for their actions, which is why they were commanded to leave the Garden of Eden.

I am ready to be held accountable. I realize that the Messiah, like the great biblical figures in this room, has to be held to a higher standard.

*Jacob:* Yoseph, you don't have to pack your bags just yet. I'll withhold personal judgment, based upon your answer. You have been truthful, and G-d values truth and sincerity above all else. If G-d finds this in a person, He seeks them out. He cherishes sinners that have repented, like you, or individuals who have found themselves in dire or difficult straits, like my grandfather, Abraham, or the prophet Moses. If you are true in your heart and, above all, live by the Ten Commandments, you will make the right choices in life. You will be held to the highest of standards, as was Moses, if you become the Messiah.

*King David:* As you know, Yoseph, when G-d chose me to be the second king of Israel, He looked into my heart and saw truth. However, I betrayed His trust. Because of my lust for Bat Sheba, I committed adultery, and I deliberately set the stage for her husband to die in battle. I broke two of the Ten Commandments, and I was punished with many years of illness for my sins. Although I repented, I am accountable to myself and eternally in human history. I did, as king, try my best to do good things for my people. However, I can never be the Messiah. I don't know who can be, given our imperfect human makeup.

I felt sorry for David. He was the greatest of kings. The interview seemed irrelevant. I was tired and I needed to preserve my strength. Michael sensed my fatigue, and we took an afternoon break. All I wanted was a Coke Zero. I settled for a glass of water that had the sweetest of tastes. Thirty minutes later, the questioning began again.

The interview resumed with Methuselah asking me why we can't understand G-d's ways. I think he was trying to be gentle on me after the previous tough questions of his colleagues. His temperament was so much like my grandfather's.

*Yoseph:* There has to be a mystery and wonder about G-d. The sages say that Moses understood forty-nine of fifty levels of the Almighty. He did not understand the Essence of G-d, the last level. Through the Creator making Himself human in His behavior to us, we gain a limited, anthropomorphic scope of His relationship to our world. Without the mystery of the Almighty's Essence, we might lose faith. Where would the human race be without faith?

*Methuselah:* Are you happy, Yoseph?

*Yoseph:* Yours is such a tough question. I'm happy with Marcia, and I'm happy with belonging to G-d. I'm not happy with the rumbling inside of me. My life beginning in the womb set up a neurosis that has damaged the joy of my being. You don't reverse that suffering, no matter how much you have achieved or how grateful you are. Compared to an individual nurtured with a loving upbringing, you can never catch up. You may never be truly joyful or have inner peace.

Rabbi Saadiah Gaon stated, "The inevitable quest for knowledge will always be a cause of grief and pain. The man who wishes to amass wisdom will never be content with what he has learned. The true scholar will always want to learn more." I fall into the definition of a lifelong student. I have a thirst for knowledge. Moreover, I have chosen the spiritual road, and I have a yearning for G-d. Following such a difficult path is more demanding than anything I have ever attempted or done in my entire life. Reaching the top of Jacob's ladder seems insurmountable. To be the Messiah will leave little time for joy. I do find joy in being in Florida's nature preserves, where I can walk outdoors and observe the birds and turtles. We always seem to be marching toward something, but we never seem to arrive.

*Methuselah:* Happiness is often an illusion. Now, can you shed some light on aging?

*Yoseph:* I accept that you are 969 years old. There may be a number of reasons why you and other biblical figures like Seth lived to such ages, not the least of which is G-d providing miracles to humankind. Abraham's wife Sarah gave birth at age ninety while Abraham was one hundred. G-d restored Sarah's youth and hormones in order for Sarah to become pregnant and give birth to the patriarch Isaac. Unheard of years ago, today women in their sixties have given birth to children.

G-d told Adam that because of His sins, his promised lifespan would not be. G-d has always showed His enormous patience with humankind. He gradually decreased man's age, until we reach Moses living to 120 years and King David living to the biblical age of seventy. When evil entered the world after the sin in the Garden of Eden, G-d may have needed to lower the age in order for evil men not to live long enough to deify themselves.

As a scientist, I can only offer some hypothetical arguments. There is reasonable evidence that years ago, the oxygen concentration was about 40 percent compared to today's content of 18 percent in the air. In polluted environments, the oxygen concentration can dip into single digits. Oxygen is our hidden immune system and the only molecule able to burn toxins in our cells, providing that sufficient oxygen concentrations exist in the cells. This is especially relevant in our modern world, in which the challenges to our bodily organs keep rising. The higher the concentrations of oxygen in our cells, within limits, the better our health. Perhaps, as was suggested by Tennyson, the atmospheric pressure of oxygen before Noah's Ark and the great Flood was significantly higher than that after the Flood because of a changed sea level. With a higher atmospheric pressure, more oxygen would be taken in with each breath, like in hyperbaric chambers. Back in biblical days, that oxygen would find itself in very high concentrations in our cells. Cancer and heart disease, our two biggest killers, would not be evident.

Our mitochondrial organelles in our cells, which are responsible for consuming our oxygen to provide energy, likely were present in much higher concentrations in our cells in biblical times. This was necessary to accommodate the increased oxygen. Also, with a natural diet, free of preserved foods, there would be little or probably no free radicals to attack our mitochondria. With regard to diet, it has been suggested that the diet before the Flood was strictly vegetarian. Pesticides, of course, had not been introduced. It was only after the Flood with Noah's sacrifice of animals, when G-d permitted humans to eat animals. Gradually, with the corruption of the diet, the lifespan decreased. Abraham came in on the scene some three hundred years after the Flood and died at 175. Moses, who came another five hundred years after Abraham, lived to 120.

A diet of oxygen, natural foods, whole grain bread, and natural oils combined with pure water and an unpolluted environment would be favorable to aging and longevity. Today's mass farming has stripped the earth of essential minerals. Animal protein has re-supplied these minerals that are required for our enzyme and protein systems to operate; however, we have paid a price once we started to inject the animals with antibiotics, hormones, and steroids. When we consume the animal, we consume these diet additives, which can affect our cells to increase their rates of cell division. Cells have a limited lifespan, so we age faster. Cells that mature faster are subject to more mutations and we to earlier illnesses.

Scientists, in recent years, have used sophisticated molecular biology technology to determine the good genes that turn on and the bad genes that turn off so that increases in the aging process can be observed. Ongoing experiments include not only laboratory mice and rats, but also primates like chimpanzees. The results show that the human lifespan one day might be increased to 150 years. Lowering your caloric intake slows down multiplication of your cells, as well as turning on good genes and turning off bad genes. Animals on caloric restriction do not get tumors as early as those on full diets. How important this was in biblical times is not known. The sweet taste could be satisfied by natural dates, figs, and berries instead of the refined white sugar and sugar substitutes that we consume today. Research has demonstrated the damaging effects of sugar on the heart, and perhaps on cancer.

When all is said and done, I prefer the spiritual argument to the scientific one, even though I am a member of the latter group. G-d granted length of days to you, Methuselah, and to others like Seth and Adam to show His mastery of our world and universe through Divine Providence. When He performs His magic, we become skeptical of His miracles because He does it in a fashion that we draw conclusions of events based upon the laws of nature. This was true during the parting of the Sea of Reeds during the Exodus from Egypt, and even in part with the Egyptian plagues. Pharaoh's wizards were able to duplicate Moses' first two plagues, and the Pharaoh thought that Moses' was using astrology and the placement of the stars to perform his sorcery. When the wizards could not duplicate the plague of darkness and the later plagues, they told the Pharaoh that Moses was acting under the Hand of G-d. Despite the evidence, Pharaoh was unsuccessful in his blatant attempts to defy G-d. He lost his entire army when the Sea of Reeds parted and then resealed itself via G-d's Divine Providence.

There is a reference in the Book of Daniel to immortality, beginning for the faithful righteous at Judgment Day, the end of life as we know it now but not the end. G-d tells Daniel, who, along with Jacob, knew the time when this life would be completed and a new Messianic Age would begin, that the matters were to be obscured and sealed until the Time of the End. G-d speaks about a time of 1,290 years, which some sages throughout the centuries have erroneously used to calculate the End Time. In the same verse, G-d also speaks about the worthiness of reaching 1,345 years. I look at these numbers as a riddle that can be interpreted to mean that the Messianic Age will last between 1,290 and 1,345 years, even longer than the age of you, Methuselah.

Can one imagine living that long? It would seem like an eternity, like the immortality that Daniel predicted for the fortunate survivors of this world. Why did G-d pick these numbers? Well according to my whacky hypothesis, the 1,290 to 1,345 years represents the life of a tree—perhaps a biblical olive tree. In the Book of Isaiah, *Isaiah 65:22*, we find a Messianic reference quote, *"They shall not build another inhabit, they shall not plant another eat; for as the days of a tree shall be the days of My people, and My chosen shall long endure their handiwork."* Trees vary in their lifespan considerably, and you can find trees on this earth more than 1,345 years old.

*Methuselah:* An interesting, unproven hypothesis, Yoseph. You do underscore and explain my original query with respect to longevity. It is said that Einstein realized that you can never solve a problem at the level it was created. You must step outside of yourself, your mind, and your ego. You have stepped out of yourself and your mind with your theory, but I do still detect ego. It is imperative, almost obsessive, for you to be the first to propose an original idea and make sure you get credit for it. Am I right?

How do they read into me? How do they all know? I can't hide anything from the magnificent seven.

*Yoseph:* Yes, you are right, Methuselah. There is ego involved in the way you stated. I have made progress. However, there is still a residual need to feel special because of the almost total void of demonstrable love and praise in my upbringing. When this is missing and you don't express your feelings, your hurts, and needs, then being made to feel special by Marcia and even the Creator will not be enough. I don't know if we are born with a need for recognition. We might be. In my case, part of the quest to be original in my thinking and, furthermore, to be the Messiah is strictly for me. I have tamed my neurosis considerably, and I am much more in tune with the love of my family, friends, and the Creator. I do have the strongest desire to give back to my Creator for what He has given me. I hope to show all of you this in my answers to your questions during this amazing interview process. I thank you all for giving me this opportunity. I shall cherish these times with all of you for my remaining days.

If my aging hypothesis is incorrect, so be it. When it comes to the Messianic Age, there are a lot of riddles. One thing that is clear is that there will be resurrection, and all of you of course will be back on earth to assist the Messiah, whoever that will be. Your reward, and that of Daniel, will be living again, on earth, in the special times to come.

I just wanted to add one point. At the time Daniel lived, there were only Jews and idol-worshipping nations. Urbanization had started in Mesopotamia and in Egypt five thousand years ago, but there was a lack of spirituality in these cultures, and as time progressed, a disrespect for G-d. Had only these cultures continued, there would be no civilization as we know it today, because too much evil would have dominated the world.

G-d knew we needed His Torah, so 3,300 years ago, He came into public view in front of 600,000-plus Jews at Mount Sinai. There, He presented the Israelites with His Ten Commandments. G-d's Torah did not just create civilization; it *was* civilization. It was transmitted before the Jews, under Joshua, then conquered the land occupied by idol-worshipping Canaanites. The Torah, given in an isolated barren desert, was a prerequisite to the State of Israel, which is a reversal of the usual practice. Most countries exist before their leaders write their doctrines.

There were no Christians, Buddhists, Hindus, Taoists, and Muslims, etc. The chosen people were the Jews, who were selected to carry the spiritual banner of G-d to all humankind. I reiterate that *chosen* to me means that all deserving good people of all faiths and beliefs shall be either living or resurrected to receive their reward of entering a new life in the Messianic Age.

The Book of Leviticus in the Torah clearly states that the promised life for walking in G-d's path applies to humans of all faiths, and not solely to the Jews. *Psalm 33* in King David's Book of Psalms confirms that righteous people of all faiths and beliefs will enter G-d's gates. Nor will G-d's kindness be bestowed upon the Jewish people exclusively, but will be received by all who are good and straightforward in their hearts, (*Psalms 125*) who merit it (*Leviticus 25*).

*King David:* We adjourn our interview until tomorrow. Michael will escort you to your lodgings.

*Michael:* There is a season to work and a time to rest. It's time for quiet and peacefulness and joy.

We walked south for about a mile through the perfumery gardens of the Temple Mount. When I looked up, I realized that the precious puffy white clouds that I had visualized earlier in our approach to the Third Temple were actually a miraculous reflection from the sky below. Space was infinite in heaven. I thought how much fun our Nobel Prize physicists would have here answering new questions about the universe from a perspective in heaven. Perhaps they might even unlock the mysterious moments before the Big Bang.

I thought my eyes were playing tricks on me. With my cataract surgery and new crystal lenses inserted into my eyes, I felt so grateful to visualize the incredible magnificence of the green, rolling hills and pristine, gentle flowing brooks. Birds were everywhere and chirping their songs. I saw my favorite great white egret fly in front of us. In the distance, there were flocks of ducks and small and large blue herons. Lyme Disease-free golden deer and caramel-colored dwarf rabbits scampered by as we strolled.

I can't describe the freedom I felt. I had been living so long in my tense, restricted body. I thought back to those awful days in the psychiatric wards, where the door closed and I was trapped inside. How awful it must be in prison. Thank G-d there would be no need for prisons in the Messianic Age.

I was so enthralled with the breathtaking beauty of this heavenly Shangri-La that I neglected to notice the blue rays being emitted from the sun. It was a reminder of eight years past, when I saw blue rays along with white rays on our vacation drive from Florida to New York. Daylight wasn't quite daylight. I realized that there was a calming bluish tint in the air, and Michael told me that there is no darkness in heaven. Rather, the heavens are powder blue during daylight and take on a deeper blue hue with evening. I thought of the End of Days, when there will be a twenty-four-hour period just like this one—neither normal day or night.

I couldn't believe the house. It was adjacent to the Temple Mount, set beside a lake just like our Florida home—an identical replica. All your dreams come true in heaven. As we entered the house, I glanced all round at the familiar surroundings. Our same paintings were on the walls, as were all of the wonderful choices of furniture that Marcia had made in decorating our home.

Music resounded from our family room as Kenny Rogers sang *Through the Years*. Marcia and I always loved to dance to Kenny's song. We would snuggle in real close on the dance floor and just rock erotically without moving while we tasted each other's lips. When I was a teenager, I used to go to the YMHA dances in Toronto, and we shag-danced to the music of the song *In the Still of the Night*. My dancing today is a carryover from the fifties.

I suddenly sighed, as my beautiful Marcia wasn't with me to share the experience. Michael saw the vacancy in my eyes. "Look through the arch," he instructed me. And there she was, more beautiful than the day I met her. I read that when G-d sends a soul down to earth, he splits it into two irregular halves. The greatest blessing on earth is to find your other jagged half, your soul mate. Not easy to do. We ran to each other and I swept her off her feet, smothering her in kisses. Her mouth was delicious, and the breath coming out of her nose was so sensual that I immediately felt like rushing her off to the bedroom. I turned to Michael a little embarrassed, and he was beaming.

I cleared my throat and introduced Marcia to Michael. He genuinely smiled. When Marcia offered dinner, he smiled again. "We angels only live on Manna," Michael said. "Yes, the same Manna that G-d fed the Israelites for forty years in their wondering in the Sinai Desert. It provides sufficient nourishment to sustain us and has a rather exotic taste." I thanked Michael profusely for being so kind. He took his leave and told me he would come by around nine o'clock in the morning. He said that G-d knew we would be happy with the banquet He provided for Marcia and me. G-d knew that we loved French food, and we dined and wined that evening in sumptuous ecstasy, and made love.

Before I drifted off to my best night of sleep ever, I thought of Marcia, G-d, Michael, the day's happenings, the Princes, the Temple Mount, G-d's Holy Temple, and a quote from a biblical commentator.

*"For a trivial goal, any hardship is great; for a great goal, any hardship is trivial."*

I was interviewing to become King Messiah of Israel. This was my final goal. All that I had done in my life seemed to have nothing to do with this goal. I remembered another biblical quote.

*"Before a final goal can be realized, there is a long list
of tasks that seemingly have no relationship to the goal,
but they are indispensable to its attainment."*

I had been wondering through my own Sinai Desert for sixty-six years. The Rebbe Schneerson had told me through his published letters that I would take on another mission in addition to being a husband, father, and spiritual human being. I thought the mission was promoting the building of G-d's Third Temple. Indeed it was. What better than to have the Messiah build the Temple, as the great sage Maimonides suggested. I thought that the challenges we faced in our world were daunting. Getting our world prepared to enter the Messianic Age was equally, if not more, difficult.

An important part of my task as the Messiah would be to bring all Jews together, an essentially failed task, since the destruction of David and Solomon's First Temple 2,500 years ago. Without humanity lining up behind G-d and the building of His Third Temple, I dreaded the real possibility that the Messianic Age would not come about through the harmony and peacefulness of humankind. Instead, we would face apocalyptic events, predicted by the Hebrew Bible and the New Testament at the End of Days.

Somewhere in my mind, I knew I might be asked to address the concept of Jesus returning to be the Messiah. I thought surely that Jesus would have to be one of the finalists. How could Christianity, a major constituency of the world population, be appeased? I wondered who else had been interviewed. So many remarkable men and women had lived throughout the ages, although there seemed to be no one outstanding on the horizon. I drifted off to sleep.

# 13

# CHANOCH

*WE COULD ALMOST TOUCH* the sun. The water in our kidney-shaped pool was glistening like reflected diamonds. Marcia and I sat in white, painted wicker on our aluminum screened-in patio drinking a cup of celestial tea watching the sunrise over the easterly horizon. A pair of bluebirds swooped down to our red bottlebrush tree and nibbled at the premium finch food in our bronze hot air balloon-shaped bird feeder. It was a beautiful morning, a perfect day for an interview. We sat in silence, holding hands until Michael appeared. It was 9:00 A.M. on the button, and it was time to go. Marcia sensed my nervousness and gave my hand a gentle squeeze to assure me that I would be all right, no matter the outcome.

Last night, we drank far too much, and found ourselves jubilantly laughing and acting silly about my keeping company with angels and Princes. Marcia played all the different Princes, giggling in a husky voice, while I pleaded my case to be the Messiah. Strangers back on earth would not believe me if I told them my story. Heaven! Are you kidding? Pay no attention to Yoseph's exaggerated ramblings. It's his bipolar disorder acting up again.

I had asked Marcia how she got to heaven. She said that she didn't know. She had lain down to take a nap on the couch yesterday afternoon, and the last thing she remembered was being gently lulled into a subliminal trans-like state. Oh! There it is, I thought. The Creator was working His miracles. G-d would come to His prophets when He either hypnotized them into a trans-like state or visited them in their subconscious dreams. Moses was the only Hebrew prophet who remained wide awake while G-d spoke to him.

Michael beckoned, and I blew a kiss to my *bashert*, my soul mate. Michael had a surprise for me this morning. He looked elegant in his draping white cloak, wrapped round with a golden-roped sash. "Grab on Yoseph," he said, "today you fly." As we soared into the sky, the tension in every muscle in my body let go. I felt liberated, after two-thirds of a century of being shackled in neurotic chains. I realized what the inanimate Statue of Liberty in New York's harbor has been trying to tell us all these years. Freedom is G-d-given. Nobody has a right to take it from you. If you want to recoup your freedom, you must not only win it back but you must also feel and internalize your freedom in the most central core of your being, your Divine Soul. Otherwise, you will remain enslaved, as I have been during my lifetime.

As we glided over the splendor of the grounds of the Temple Mount, I sensed that my guardian angel, Michael, had something special to show me. It was only with an aerial view that you could visualize the Temple's shape in the figure of a man. The Sanctuary, where we held the Messiah Interviews, and the Holy of Holies containing the Ark of the Testimony, represented the neck and head, respectively, while the entrance hall intersecting with the westerly wall of the Inner Courtyard had the appearance of shoulders. There were four great chambers, each three levels in height, containing thirty-three cubicles. You would swear that these chambers made up the two arms and two legs of a man. The boundaries of the body were defined by the perimeter of the Inner Courtyard, which I recognized from the air as enclosing the sacrificial altar and the Levites' *duchan* platform.

When we touched down on the marble stone floor of the Inner Courtyard, we were once again treated to the melodious sounds of the Levite Priests, singing their songs and playing their musical instruments. As we walked up the eight steps of Mount Moriah to enter the Hall leading to the Inner Sanctuary, I felt chills in my soul, privileged and honored to stand in the Holy awesomeness of G-d's place. I imagined that the ancient Jews must have felt the same way when they entered Solomon's Temple and felt G-d's *Shechinah*, His Divine Presence. The Third Temple on earth would offer such ecstasy again.

There was an unbeatable aroma in the air. It was the smell of the multiple spices of burning incense. Yesterday was such an anxiety-ridden session that I didn't really see the Sanctuary. Today, both my eyes and brain visualized the beautiful simplicity of this Holy chamber. The oil lamps of the golden Menorah were aglow, bringing eternal light to our world below. We took our seats and waited for the courageous Princes to enter the room. Within a minute or two, these great men appeared and the semicircular table was full. All eyes were on me. King David turned the interview over to Chanoch as all bid me good morning.

I had forgotten to pray to the Creator for strength, so I closed my eyes for a moment and found myself walking gracefully in the gardens of the Temple Mount. As I had done many times prior to a blood pressure reading in the doctor's office, I imagined G-d's white light coming down through the trees to embrace my being.

*Chanoch:* Good morning, Yoseph.

I responded in kind. His first question was oddly enough to ask me why the Temple was shaped in the figure of a man.

Not a coincidence, I reflected, considering that I was being interviewed by seven mind readers who could see into the truthfulness or falseness of my heart. I looked at Michael on my left, and his smile told me that he had expected Chanoch's first question. It was Michael's way of starting the interview on a level playing field by taking away the element of surprise. I knew that Chanoch could not decipher the thoughts of angels, but mine apparently were an open book. I sensed that Chanoch genuinely wanted to give me every opportunity to succeed.

I took a deep breath and replied.

*Yoseph:* I can't speak for what G-d intended. Yet, I can't help thinking that man and G-d can never be mutually exclusive. What I mean by this comment is that G-d created man not to be His servant and follow His Will, as is believed by Orthodox Judaism. Rather, the term *servant* implies that man become a partner and merge with G-d. I don't believe that G-d is the puppeteer, pulling the strings to make man dance to His merry tune. I think it's more G-d's predestined plan for Creation that He and man make symphonic music together.

In the Sinai Desert, Moses and the Israelites honored G-d by building a Tabernacle so that G-d could dwell among them. Five hundred years later, David and Solomon did the same through the grandeur of the First Temple. At the End of Days, we shall have thrice honored G-d's Shechinah with a Third Temple, a duplicate of this magnificent edifice in heaven. G-d, in turn, has honored man by choosing man among all species to share His Covenant of a brighter world in which so much is possible. Only humans have been granted the gift of free will. The figure of man in the Temple is symbolic of G-d's dedication to the Covenant enterprise.

*Chanoch:* I like your answer, Yoseph. I don't think I've heard any of our interviewees put it quite like that. I have a less straightforward question for you. Why did G-d remove me alive from the earth? As you know, He did the very same thing with Elijah the prophet when He was alive. Elijah perhaps I can give reasons for, but not for me. In both our cases, not only did our souls ascend intact but so did our bodies.

My colleagues in this forum are quite different than me in this respect, or are they? Their souls came to heaven when their bodies gave way and were interred in the earth. G-d has resurrected them as whole souls with body because the Creator needs them to be ready to go at any moment. It is written by the Hebrew prophets that the Messianic Age can come about at any time if the human race is ready. What does being ready mean to you?

*Yoseph:* Your first question is most baffling, especially in view of all of you being Princes who will assist the Messiah at the Time of the End. Why the distinction between death and life, if we arrive at the same place in the End? The only answer that makes any sense to me is that it was important for G-d to show His omnipotence and His unique mastery of the world.

G-d created the Universe, *ex nihilo*, out of nothing, although our Greek philosophers and skeptics throughout the ages might easily argue that the world always existed and that humanity evolved during the course of evolution. I previously wrote in my book, *Divinely Inspired*, that I believe G-d is the master scientist, responsible for both Creation and evolution. I'll briefly summarize.

Even the most devout supporters of Darwinian evolution cannot adequately explain organic multicellular life. Which came first? The chicken or the egg? You need the chicken to lay the egg; however, the egg has to hatch to create the chicken. One of them was the original, but which one? Humans make proteins and DNA, and each are similarly a necessity for the other. Proteins are created from our DNA, and DNA is created from our protein molecules. Like the chicken and the egg, which came first? Scientists have never been able to duplicate G-d's feat of creating Adam, *ex nihilo*, out of nothing in their research laboratories.

*Chanoch:* If I may, I would like to nutshell summarize the concept you have put forward, in two sentences:

*"Man achieves the possible. G-d accomplishes the impossible."*

Can you elaborate, Yoseph?

Why didn't I think of this quote? Simple, yet brilliant and profound. I assimilated my thoughts for a moment, and then understood that Chanoch was asking me to make the case for G-d. I also realized that, although these giants of men could read my mind, they may not be acquainted with the nuances of the modern world, post-biblical times. Yet, all that I could rely on for my answer were biblical miracles.

*Yoseph:* If I may, I would like to illustrate my answer in chronological order.

The Princes nodded.

*Yoseph:* Only G-d knows what happened moments before the Big Bang initiated our universe, since He alone was responsible for these moments. The Almighty always leaves room for us to doubt by frequently providing an alternative, natural scientific explanation for His miracles. As Master Scientist, He leaves it up to, and assists, human scientists to make discoveries of His scientific world. G-d gave humans unique qualities of thought, language, superior intellect, doubt, and imagination in granting us the gift of life. The doubt allows us to exercise our G-d-given free will and is aimed at the disinterested party who is least willing to accept the Omnipotence, Omniscience, and Omnipresence of a Supreme Being. G-d transcends time and space. He was, He is, and He will be. He is the First Cause, as Marcia always reminds me. He is the Infinite One, and His roots are ancient. He existed before the Creation of the Universe, when He alone was present. At some point, G-d created the angels to assist Him in His plan for humankind.

The physicist Isaac Newton looked past his physics to conclude that our stars and planets were aligned precisely to permit human life on earth. Even the slightest deviation would have been problematic for life to exist. Our bodies function in a narrow temperature range, which would not have been possible had the earth been located anywhere else in three-dimensional space than it presently is. Furthermore, Einstein knew that his Theory of Relativity could help explain our world, but he too came to the conclusion that there wouldn't be a world without the Creator. These Nobel Prize-winning physicists proved that Faith can stand alongside Reason.

I believe, as I wrote in *Divinely Inspired*, that G-d gave us the Seven Days of Creation 5,669 years ago to provide us with order, structure, and time. All the important elements of our modern world were described in those Seven Days—water, air, land, planetary structures, heaven, earth, flora and fauna, light and darkness, marine life, animals, and humans. Examined in this light, there is no discrepancy between a relatively recent biblical Creation and a fifteen-billion-year-old universe, or a four-and-a-half-billion-year-old earth. G-d was the pioneer of numerology in our world with the prime numbers one through seven. He was the One who coined the term *day*, which everyone in the world uses. The seventh day of rest, which G-d may or not have needed for Himself—perhaps He could have created the world in an instant—has evolved into our weekend of extended work, joy, relaxation, reflection, and prayer.

Thus, the Seven Days of Creation and the billions of years of evolution are mirror images in G-d's unlimited, infinite wisdom, which He uses to stimulate man's intellectual interpretations of life. In contrast, man's vision is limited. His brain normally seeks to separate the different time periods of Creation and evolution when they are actually one and the same in G-d's Eyes.

Many of G-d's achievements will never be duplicated by humans. Adam, the first biblical man, was created miraculously by the Almighty from the earth's dust without the normal fertilization of an egg and a sperm, and he came onto this earth as an already grownup youth. Biologists have not yet created human beings, but they have achieved the possible by cloning animals. We should give credit where credit is due. G-d was the first molecular biologist, cloning Eve from Adam's rib.

One valid argument that scientists espouse is that Creationists are narrow-minded toward evolution, although some in the biblical field have proposed Intelligent Design as an alternative *scientific* hypothesis There is no doubt in my mind that humans evolved through evolution approximately 100,000 to 150,000 years earlier than Adam. Alfred Wallace, a contemporary of Darwin, believed that the human anatomy and brain were too advanced to have developed from Darwin's natural selection process, whereby one species follows sequentially from another. If you carefully examine the intricacies of human morphology, biochemistry, physiology, and pharmacology, it is a stretch, in my mind, that evolution can successfully explain the sophistication of human beings at the cellular level.

Anthropological genetic studies are tracing the geographical patterns and movements of evolutionary humans. Modern genetics has been able to define these movements and patterns based upon distinct individual and group DNA laboratory measurements. We know that the DNA of Evolutionary Man existed long before Adam. However, with Creation Man, G-d seemed to have endowed Adam with these same genetic properties. I have had my own DNA tested, and I belong to groups who lived perhaps sixteen thousand years ago, at least ten thousand years before Adam. Yet, as a Jew, I came from the lineage of Adam. Modern populations have been tested to determine if they are descendants of the *kohanim*, or high priests of Israel. It was Moses' brother, Aaron, who was picked by G-d to be the first high priest. Genetic studies have intriguingly suggested that the *kohanim* are of more recent origin, within the time frame of Creation Human, rather than Evolution Man.

As I discussed in depth in *Divinely Inspired*, why create the Creation Man, Adam, at all? Until biblical Creation, Evolutionary Man was scattered in rural populations throughout our world. According to Egyptian history, man existed in Egypt before Adam. Shortly after the Creation of Adam, villages, towns, and cities sprung up in Egypt and Mesopotamia to initiate geographical civilization. Population increased as these agrarian societies learned how to store food so that man did not have to pick berries and hunt for his meat as marauding bands on the wilds of the savanna. Geographical Civilization is not Spiritual Civilization. The latter began with the pronouncements of the Ten Commandments at Mount Sinai. Adam's *birth* was a prerequisite along this path, as this time period of geographical civilization set the stage for good and evil. From Adam to Abraham, evil prevailed. Goodness began with Abraham and belief in One G-d and then stood on equal footing with evil when the Ten Commandments were given at Mount Sinai.

We can observe many of G-d's miracles in biblical times, like angels, Methuselah's age, Chanoch taken alive to heaven, Noah's Ark and the Flood, Sarah giving birth at age ninety, the Egyptian plagues that Pharaoh's sorcerers found impossible to duplicate, the parting of the Sea of Reeds, the Ten Commandments, Joshua making the sun stand still, Joshua conquering the idol-worshipping Canaanites with almost no loss of life during a period of seven years of war, G-d's Divine Presence in the Temple, prophesy, revival of the dead by the prophets, and the miracle of Purim.

Miracles cannot explain science. Neither can scientists explain miracles. Skeptics and scoffers can dismiss miracles, but I think they do so at their own peril. Perhaps the only way they can alter their belief system is with the appearance of G-d Himself. G-d may be closer to doing just that, sooner than later. Maybe it's time for atheists to tone down their rhetoric, humbly subdue yet maintain their intellect, and give themselves an opportunity to be part of the wondrous World to Come: the Messianic Age.

Abraham spoke for the first time. A deep baritone voice emerged from his mouth. His eyes were gentle, and I felt at ease. He was all kindness, yet very wise.

*Abraham:* Yoseph, your love for your Creator screams out in your words and beliefs. From my personal experience, G-d leads people in the direction they wish to go. To use a modern expression, "You can lead a horse to water, but you can't make it drink." My advice to you, Yoseph, is that until G-d decides to show Himself, forget about the skeptics and scoffers. It is human nature to attack when either old ideas are challenged or new ideas are proposed. People feel inferior, become intimidated, and are reluctant to give up their power base. You are smart enough to know from your Primal Therapy that people are incapable or do not desire to change their temperament and character. "What you see is what you get." As Kenny Rogers sang in *Gambler*, you have to know when to hold them and you have to know when to fold them and walk away.

*Yoseph:* Thank you, Abraham. I've always had that problem. I just don't know when to quit.

*Chanoch:* Before we speak about Resurrection, can you answer my second question? What does being ready for the Messianic Age mean to you?

*Yoseph:* In my mind, it means that the Jews must be ready, but we are not.

The First Temple was destroyed by the Babylonians because our ancestors lost sight of their morality and turned away from the Ten Commandments. The Jews committed murder, adultery, and thievery.

The Romans destroyed the Second Temple because we Jews forgot our Covenant to be a kingdom of priests. Greek philosophical influence took its toll on our belief in G-d, and we chose not to treat our fellow Jews with respect and dignity. Diversity and disagreement is healthy, but not in an insincere society in which everyone is out for themselves and will not hesitate to trample you if you stand in their way.

We disgraced the Creator, and we even murdered G-d's prophets inside the Temple.

When prophesy and idol worship disappeared, the rabbis and sages at the crossroads of the common era saved Judaism. This, in my opinion, has been a mixed blessing, because we moved from a society based upon the unity of the Twelve Tribes, representing Judaism and the Ten Commandments, to one dependent upon incorporation of the spirituality of the Ten Commandments into the Orthodox rabbinical religion of the 613 Commandments and the Oral Torah. At the End of Days, we shall somehow know which Tribe we belong to, and we shall be Jews first by division once more of the Land into the Twelve Tribes. One can honor G-d in many ways, and if I become the Messiah, I will encourage Orthodox Judaism within each Tribe for those who want this way of life.

I say this with no disrespect for my Creator or for you, Moses, but the problem is the interpretation of what's written in the Torah. G-d instructs us to follow all His commandments, statutes, and laws, and Orthodox Judaism interprets this as G-d's Will. His Will includes not only the written Torah but also the Oral Torah, as decoded and elaborated upon in the books of the Mishnah, Talmud, and Code of Jewish Laws. To be a Jew, therefore, you must adhere to all that is written, and all that was orally passed down by Moses.

I agree that the Torah cannot be detracted from, but Judaism has lost its way because of the differences in interpretation of G-d's words. Personally, there are commandments of the 613, which I desire to follow. These commandments are part of the *Shema* prayer. However, as I pointed out earlier, my interpretation of G-d's Will is about sincerity in your heart. If you are not true of heart, all the religion in the world will not help you to acquire favor with G-d. I interpret following all His commandments, statutes, and laws as adhering to the Ten Commandments and walking the walk of life with truth in one's heart.

I was expecting Moses to weigh in heavily after I had just insulted him. I was bracing myself for his anger; Moses was capable of more than anger. I knew the feelings of rage from my experiences in Primal Therapy. I suppressed my rage in the womb and in life, but the quiet, humble man, Moses, with the speech impediment, minced no words. He let his rage fly, and rightly so, when he saw that the Israelites had taken all of their gold, melted it down, and constructed the Golden Calf. Enraged, he smashed the First Set of Tablets inscribed with the Ten Commandments.

*Moses:* Do you have the audacity to challenge G-d and His Will? Are you that insolent? And why, in G-d's Name, are you not showing the highest level of respect? Are you questioning my writing of the Torah, as do Conservative and Reform Jews? Are you calling me a liar?

Dead silence in the Sanctuary. I looked over at Michael, but he was blankly staring straight ahead. Had I jumped off the precipice? It was like my 1995 suicide attempt. I had swallowed two hundred pills and then realized I could not roll back the clock and change my mind. My words were out there, and it was too late to take them back. If I did, I would be a hypocrite by not speaking the truth in my heart. I was hoping I could feel G-d's energy in the room, but I could not. Was G-d hanging me out to dry?

*Yoseph:* Moses, I certainly am sorry for anything I said that has offended or hurt you. I totally believe that you wrote

the Torah and that all that is written in the Torah was from
G-d's very Mouth when you were with Him on the top of
Mount Sinai.

In his modern online forum, Rabbi Simon Jacobson
writes that there are two schools of Torah thought: self-
abnegation and self-actualization. Self-abnegation requires
subjugation of one's own will in obedient observance to
G-d's Will that we follow all His commandments, statutes, and laws. Self-actualization allows one to pursue one's
own individual path to faith as set out by the creation of
humans in the Divine Image. I accept self-abnegation, but
favor self-actualization as a means of leading the believer
to a Higher calling.

Therefore, I am not challenging the words of the Torah.
I am challenging the application of the words, maybe not
for this world, but as they might better apply to the next
world, the Messianic Age. I don't pretend to understand G-d's
Essence, and maybe strict adherence to the religion is what He
intended for the biblical Jews and later generations. Perhaps
it's all part of His plan to proceed from an imperfect world
to a more perfect one. I just don't think it's a good idea for
the Messianic Age. I can't see Jews coming together if strict
adherence to the religion is going to be the criteria for being
defined as a Jew.

The Messianic Age, for me, represents a freedom of spirit. I
recognize, however, that internal balance has to be set, because
too much freedom of the spirit can lead your soul to be on
fire and to delusions of grandeur. I ask you why we haven't as
yet entered the redemptive period. It's a rhetorical question. I
believe it's because, although the rabbis saved Judaism, they

also unintentionally set the stage for division among the Jewish people. Without unity of the Jews, how can the world and we be ready for the Messianic Age on any moment's notice from the Almighty? The only conclusion I can draw is that the Messianic Age will come at its appointed time. Regrettably, the Time of the End will then be apocalyptic, with brimstone and fire seen on a magnitude never observed before in human history. The Hebrew Bible and the New Testament in the Christian Bible are clear on this.

I stand on record with the principles I espouse. If this is a deal breaker, so be it. We can stop now.

Moses was still not happy, but he had calmed down as if overcome by Divine thoughts. I recognized the aura.

*Moses:* I am feeling G-d's energy informing me that we should continue the interview process.

I was taken by surprise and looked perplexed. Moses, sensing my confusion, spoke further.

*Moses:* Yoseph, it's the same energy that a blind Isaac felt when he knew he was being tricked into giving his blessing to Jacob. Isaac's son, Esau, the firstborn, was entitled to receive the blessing, not Jacob. Rebecca, Isaac's wife, had dressed Jacob up in Esau's clothing to fool her blind husband while Esau was out hunting for a delicacy for his father. Isaac was as fine a Patriarch as his father Abraham and his son Jacob, and his spiritual discipline told him that G-d wanted His Covenant to pass through Jacob and not his twin brother, Esau.

Yoseph, you are no Isaac. However, you have some gumption, and you are developing into a man whose word is his bond. Sincere words are important, but we all know that action is where the action is.

Everyone in the room, including me, was relieved. Chanoch asked the next question. The morning was almost over, thank G-d. Michael offered me some water for my nervous throat, and then we continued.

*Chanoch:* Please comment further on Resurrection.

*Yoseph:* In *Daniel 12:13*, G-d tells Daniel, *"And as for you, go to the end; you will rest and arise to your lot at the End of the Days."* G-d doesn't tell Daniel that he will enter the Messianic Age. Daniel will be resurrected, as will everyone, to face his judgment by G-d. Each one of us will be accountable for our moral choices.

In *Daniel 12:1-3*, Daniel gives us insight into what is in store for us. Daniel's visions are both incredible and frightening:

*"And at that time, Michael the great prince shall stand up. And it shall be a time of trouble such as never was ever since there was a nation until that time. And at that time, my people shall be delivered, all those who shall be written in the book. And many of them that sleep in the dust of the earth shall awake, some to eternal life and some to reproaches and everlasting abhorrence. And the wise shall be resplendent as the splendor of the firmament and they that turn many to righteousness as the stars forever and ever."*

In *Isaiah 26:19*, the prophet Isaiah, who was murdered in the Temple by the king's guards, sings:

*"The dead shall live
My corpse shall arise
Awake and sing*

*You dweller of dust*
*For a dew of light is thy dew*
*And the earth shall bring forth the shades."*

In the Vision of the Dry Bones, *Ezekiel 37:1-14*, there is a long discourse between G-d and the prophet Ezekiel. G-d tells Ezekiel to prophesy so that the dry bones of the dead will be infused with spirit and the dead shall be resurrected and live again. G-d says that he will bring sinews and flesh to the bones and stretch the skin over the skeletons of the dead. Ezekiel observes this firsthand. G-d then breathes in a living soul, as He did with Adam, so that the resurrected individual will come to life. Your Divine Soul is the part of you that allows G-d to judge you. Finally, G-d says, *"I will open your tombs and will bring you up from your graves."*

If you believe in scriptures, and I do, it's pretty clear that Resurrection will take place for good, bad, righteous, evil, and demonic people. I should correct some of my previous inferences where I give atheists a hard time. I was referring to atheists who scoff at G-d and try to convince others to take up their same beliefs. These scoffers represent the opposite end of the spectrum, when we compare them to individuals who try to help others to have trust and faith in G-d. Daniel suggests a very good outcome for the latter group. Atheists, who live their lives righteously with sincerity in their hearts, may indeed be offered admission into the Messianic Age.

I'm not sure of the relevance of cremation with respect to Jews, since the Bible speaks of flesh being put back together with bones. Although the Messianic Age is for all peoples, the bones and flesh applies only to the restoration of Jewish people. Cremated or traditionally buried individuals in Christianity, or any other religion, may claim a different rite of passage at the End of Days.

Because G-d is eternal, the human soul is Divinely eternal. The body, on the other hand, comes from the seed of one's mother and father. The soul is called the candle of G-d, by which He examines our internal parts. Our free will determines the moral choices we make in life, which in turn may govern whether we enter the Messianic Age and eternal life.

*King David:* I'm going to interrupt the interview at this point. We have not taken a break, and it's been a long morning. In any case, we can't go any further in understanding G-d's judgment at the End of Days until Seth leads us in a discussion of good and evil this afternoon.

# 14

# MARCIA

*I WAS SITTING ON THE* verdant grass of the Temple Mount, gazing at the afternoon sky. The neat, green grass looked like a golf course, and the sky had a very slight greenish-orange tint that reminded me of the time Sean and I saw the same unusual colors in the Long Island sky. We had come out of the psychiatrist's office in Smithtown, and when we looked up at the heavens, we saw the boundaries of two orange chopsticks enclosing a thick lawn-green area. I wondered if G-d was intentionally reminding me to keep the faith.

I was exhausted from the morning session, and my only solace was to get outside and breathe the highly oxygenated unpolluted air. Michael had told me that heaven had the most ideal isothermal weather. The temperature hovered daily in the low eighties, and the air was filled with a gentle Hawaiian-like breeze of unknown origin. There were a lot of mysteries in heaven, and I found it best not to question but just to accept.

Marcia had brought a picnic lunch and some of her freshly cooked lentil soup. As I took my first spoonful, my mind wandered back to Isaac's blessing of Jacob. Poor Esau—he had to settle for Isaac's secondhand blessing, and he would not be the inheritor of G-d's Covenant with the Patriarchs. On top of this embarrassment, Esau had given up his birthright to his brother, Jacob, for essentially a pot of Jacob's freshly cooked lentil beans. I found myself feeling sorry for Esau, even though Esau later married four women from among the idol-worshipping nations. My own life seemed to be replete with lack of fairness, and so I identified with Esau's being wronged. I wondered how Jacob would respond if I were the one asking him the questions on this sensitive topic. Of course, this would not be the case. It was me who was being interviewed.

Marcia was still stunning, and she looked at least twenty years younger than her sixty-six years. The curvature of her slim body was the envy of earthly younger women, and I even noticed the Princes turning their heads in her direction to take a second look. Jacob in particular stared the longest, and I think it was because Marcia reminded him of his true love, Rachel. She was wearing a summery, bright yellow dress, and I felt so fortunate to be married twenty-five years to the girl next door.

Before I married her, when my friend Howie had asked me what it was about her that appealed to me, I gave my answer immediately. All of the five senses in Marcia turn me on. I love her smells from the exhale coming out of her nose when she kisses me. The taste of her lips is better than any sumptuous meal. Her voice is spectacular to my ears, just right in pitch and tone. Her touch stimulates every core fiber of my being. And when I see her in my mind, or like now in the flesh, I so appreciate both her outward beauty and the vivacious love of her inner soul.

Marcia is the most remarkable person I have ever known. She has the qualities of all four Matriarchs. Leah's domestic skills and kindness, Rachel's exceptional beauty, Rebecca's wisdom and determination, and Sarah's strength, assertiveness, and logic for knowing what's best spiritually and materially in life. Most precious of all, from my selfish viewpoint, she has never wavered in her love and devotion to me. I have had many troubled days, months, and yes, years, and she has stood by me always. I surely cannot say the same of myself toward her, although my love for her grows each day. I don't know if I would want to or could live life without her. It would be wonderful to be the Messiah and give back to my Creator, but only if Marcia is the queen at my side. I cherish her and am blessed.

We met in May of 1981, and married two and half years later, Christmas Eve 1983. We've had so many good times—our courtship, the honeymoon in Israel, traveling to scientific meetings all over the world, blending five children into one family, grandchildren, and friends. We can have the deepest conversation on a variety of subjects in the middle of the night.

We held hands and strolled through the Garden of Eden. I was too stressed to talk about the morning interview, so we just laughed, sang, and felt peaceful and grateful for being alive and healthy. The hour was approaching 2 P.M., so I sent her back home while I entered the Temple grounds to face Seth and the Princes.

Michael, as always, met me in the Outer Courtyard and we made our way to the Sanctuary. He offered encouragement, telling me that I was doing well. He knew that the back and forth with Moses was the most stressful part of the session, because I admired Moses so much. When we entered the Hall, Michael made a very important statement that perked up my spirits. He said that Moses does not hold grudges and that he has long forgotten the morning session, so I should do the same. I took his advice and focused on the task at hand.

I naively thought that I had achieved momentum. The mystery of G-d and the surprises of the upcoming Messiah Interviews were to shatter my ego. I heard the sounds of a marching band and walked in step to the Sanctuary. The aroma this time was the smell of freshly baked Holy bread. It was Friday, the beginning of the Jewish Sabbath.

# 15

# SETH

*IT WAS QUITE AMAZING* that the seven Princes looked as fresh as when we began the interview process. This afternoon's session would be led by Seth, the third son of Adam. Seth is the name of my biological son, the identical twin of Sean.

> *Seth:* I congratulate you, Yoseph. Most individuals never get this far in the interview process, and I never get my turn to speak.

Before I could receive Seth's praise, he quickly uttered less effusive words.

> *Seth:* At the same time, I warn you. Don't take my words as flattery. There were a handful of candidates who I have queried, and we are considering them seriously to be the Messiah. Their credentials, I'm afraid, are superior to yours. Now, tell me, Yoseph. Do you believe in fate?

Well two can play the same game. I decided to be curt. My answer was one word, clearly pronounced in a sarcastic tone.

> *Yoseph:* Yes!

*Seth:* I see that I have offended your pride. You won't be the Messiah if you give power to others over your emotions. I don't give a hoot about the reasons, Primal Therapy or Bipolar Disorder. This is serious business. You will be the spiritual leader of the free world, commanding even greater respect than the president of the United States.

*Yoseph:* (Trapped again. I then sheepishly spoke.) I'm sorry. I do believe in fate.

*Seth:* What's your fate?

*Yoseph:* To allow my fate, and my faith, to keep me on my present spiritual path, no matter the obstacles ahead. In short, to become the Messiah and not to stop trying to convince you of my passion, until I am.

*Seth:* What's my fate?

Were these interview questions or riddles I was supposed to solve? I thought for a moment.

*Yoseph:* Your fate has already been cast. With the untimely death of your brother, Abel, and later on your other brother, Cain, you were chosen by G-d to be the ancestor of Creation Human. I specify Creation, as humans already existed in the world. G-d jumpstarted evolution 3.8 billion years ago, and Evolution Human came into existence through natural selection 100,000 years ago.

*Seth:* You have it wrong, Yoseph. My father, Adam, not I, is the Father of Creation Human.

*Yoseph:* That's true, but you both played pivotal roles. Your father symbolizes the initial *goodness* in the Garden of Eden at a time when there was no *badness* or *evil* in G-d's Creation world. With the sin of your parents, Adam and Eve, evil pierced the human soul. Before this original sin, there was only one soul, created by G-d's breath into Adam's nostrils: the Divine Soul.

By the serpent's enticement of your mother with the fruit of the Tree of Knowledge, the Tree of Good and Evil, another soul entered humans. Orthodox Judaism refers to this soul as the animal soul. Your father and mother were commanded by G-d to leave the Garden of Eden, and when they did so, both the Divine Soul and the animal soul existed within them, as it does in all of humankind, ever since the original sin of your parents.

As the first ChaBaD Lubavitch Rebbe, Schneur Zalman, wisely suggested: All history, since the beginning of Creation, has been about discerning evil from good and separating the two. Further, G-d gave man free will to choose good over evil by calling upon the goodness in his Divine Soul over the badness in his animal soul. To solidify this concept, an evil Cain utilized his animal soul to murder his brother Abel because G-d praised Abel over him for their offerings. You see, Seth, I had a right to be hurt when you made me feel inferior to the other candidates.

*Seth:* It's my turn to apologize. I won't make that mistake again. Some of us are just more sensitive human beings. I have the skin of an alligator.

I see what you are driving at, Yoseph. My birth, so to speak, signaled the coming struggle for man. Good and evil choices would always exist. They would be inseparable. Man would have to make his own moral choices with his G-d-given free will.

But why would the Ancient One create a world of a mixture of the two? Why not just stay with the goodness of the Garden of Eden? Before you answer this question, you need to clarify the nature of the animal soul. Is the animal soul all bad?

*Yoseph:* No, the animal soul is a mixture of good and bad, in contrast to the Divine Soul, which can be tapped only for its goodness. Like strumming King David's harp, the more you awaken your Divine Soul, the more G-d's Light shines upon it. Goodness finds goodness, and the Light filters down to the good part of your animal soul.

The good part of the animal soul can be smothered by the bad part, and a person can become evil if he already wasn't evil to begin with. If all good is eliminated, we probably are dealing with someone who is demonic who commits mass murder of innocent people. Yet, very bad people, in rare instances, have had epiphanies in which they alter their course in life, repent their sins, and become virtuous.

Examples of the good part of the animal soul acting in the absence of the Divine Soul could be taking your children to soccer games, buying your wife flowers on Valentine's Day, contributing to society by working, following your religious beliefs, being joyful on the Sabbath, etc. In short, anything that does not involve a moral choice.

Once a moral choice to choose between right and wrong comes into play, the Divine Soul either kicks in to pass G-d's Light into the good part of the animal soul to choose good or the bad part of the animal soul is activated to choose bad, or worse, evil. Charitable gifts to help the poor and the needy involve a moral choice to do so. Orthodox Judaism speaks about an evil inclination, or *yetzer hara*, and a good inclination, or *yetzer tov*.

G-d holds us accountable over the course of our lifetimes for the moral choices we make with our gift of free will.

He will sit at the End of Days and judge each one of us, who will be resurrected. He will assess us for our moral strengths and weaknesses.

*Seth:* How will G-d do this? I'm curious to hear your answer. If you are the chosen one, we Princes will gladly help you. G-d desires that the Messiah have our assistance to implement His Judgment at the time of the future Redemption.

*Yoseph:* There is no doubt that the Divine Soul is what allows G-d to be the keeper of the scorecard. Our Divine Soul is also part of Him.

How G-d tallies up the scorecard for righteous or sinful acts is anybody's guess, because now you are within the realm of the unknown, G-d's Essence. As G-d clearly tells us in the Hebrew Bible: *"My thoughts are not your thoughts."* Man cannot see into G-d's Mind and Judgment.

*Moses:* There is a flaw in your reasoning, Yoseph. You need to return to the subject of atheists or agnostics. How can they receive Divine Light if they don't believe in a Divine Soul? Isn't that a wee-tad ironic?

*Yoseph:* I think we need to make a distinction here, because you are correct in what you say. However, do we leave out those humanists who are walking with G-d but either don't believe in Him or are sitting on the fence?

My friend Bob is such a person. He voluntarily brings dentistry to the backwoods of Guatemala, El Salvador, and Cambodia at his own expense. He is a man of peace, and he must have a Divine Soul, even if he doesn't believe he has one. Bob is living a spiritual, meaningful life, and in my opinion, he and others like him deserve entrance into the Messianic Age.

*Moses:* If that is the case then, according to your reasoning, there seems to be no advantage to living a spiritual life.

*Yoseph:* I don't feel you can take that jump. I believe that Bob is only receiving G-d's fragrance, because He chooses to be an agnostic. I may well be wrong on this. To receive His wine, you may have to believe, though your actions must be equally righteous, quality-wise, to the deeds of someone like Bob. Atheism or agnosticism, without righteousness, doesn't qualify for admission into the Garden of Eden. Neither does righteousness without sincerity of the heart. Again, that's my humble opinion. If I do become the Messiah, I will encourage G-d to not admit pious individuals, or even great Torah scholars, who on the outside spew truth but on the inside harbor false truths in their heart.

Having faith and trust in G-d, and acting in a moral manner, which He would approve of, strongly favors the expectation of receiving His help. If you don't believe in G-d, you certainly won't believe in the power of prayer to Him? Perhaps you will pray to another god, but not to the Creator. If you allow yourself to be guided by Him, I believe, your prayers will be answered. This is the wine again. And when others you don't know pray for you, G-d will ensure that those prayers are answered. "Real faith isn't simply believing that G-d can cure you of a terminal illness. True faith is believing that He will."

*Moses:* I think the panel needs to hear your exact strategy concerning the Messianic Age, since we are telling you today that you will assist G-d in the Judgment process—that is, if you are accepted by us. I have no problem with the evil or demonic persons whom G-d will resurrect to punish. They will go to *Gehinnom*, the Jewish equivalent of hell. My difficulty lies with the rest of humanity. Most people are basically good; well actually, they are a mixture of good and bad. I made this same case to G-d in the Sinai Desert, after the Israelites built the Golden Calf.

Moses doesn't pull any punches. He's a heavyweight counterpuncher, and he fires away with both hands. You dare not drop your guard.

*Yoseph:* There is no doubt that those rare humans, who are at the level of a *tzaddik*, very righteous individuals on all counts, will enter the Garden of Eden. Those who have and demonstrate their consistent actions and goodness in their hearts will enter. The majority of people are a mixture of good and bad. They can either take G-d or leave Him, depending upon which way the wind is blowing or whether it's in their interests to do so. I think that these average humans should live out their lives in this world, only. In my not-so-humble eyes, that would be fair, as G-d gives you a lifetime to improve your character. I need to emphasize that I am playing G-d here, only because you asked the question. It is really not my call. The Creator has the final say.

*Seth:* I take it, in your answer to Moses' question, that you have a vengeful streak in you. Am I correct?

*Yoseph:* You are incorrect. There has to be a division somewhere, and I don't think it can be arbitrary. I've defined the boundaries, although they may seem harsh. Moses would have been more compassionate. I guess that there is still some neurosis in me that needs the course of events to be fair and wishes justice on those who have been unfair. Why should those who have led less than exemplary or just routine ordinary lives be approved? All they've done is take and not given back.

I think G-d expects His Messiah to be tough and fair, even when it goes against his nature to be tough. Abraham proved that when he was commanded to sacrifice Isaac. Abraham remained absolutely dedicated and loyal to G-d. His faith was unshakable, and yet, he proceeded to fulfill G-d's command by going against his very nature of being kind and merciful. Killing his own son—how can one reconcile such a decision? I would give my life up for any one of my sons. My drawing a line in the sand is mild in comparison.

My insides began to boil. Seth had once again upset me with the word *vengeful*, and I wasn't fair with Abraham. I stopped myself, and I realized once again that my passion would once again get the best of me.

*Yoseph:* I'm sorry for what I just said. I apologize, Abraham. I'm probably all wrong in my assessment. Humans are imperfect and limited, as am I.

*Abraham:* Apologies accepted, though what you say is true, Yoseph. You have stood your ground, and that's admirable. I think you will be okay with the Satanic forces that lie ahead in your spiritual road. Satan, himself, will welcome a fight with you, as he is only too glad to have someone attempt to face him down. Satan and his descendants relish the challenge.

None of us are perfect, Yoseph. Like you, we all have skeletons in our closets, but you need to find a way to be more compassionate. The decision on who enters the Messianic Age is perhaps the most important decision in all of history. Moses and Seth are right. If you could let more of the Divine Light come into your heart, the bitterness of your upbringing will disappear and you will be grateful only for where you are today. You need to go against the grain in order to be the Messiah. I know that you have it in you from your own suffering. Can you give us a plan that shows your compassion? We're not talking about your childhood, when you didn't get enough love and nurturing. G-d is watching all of us here today. These interviews are not a game.

Needless to say, Abraham was right. I was still in a neurotic struggle. I responded with tears rolling down my cheeks. Michael, once again, gave me a tissue.

*Yoseph:* I have been damaged so much that my suffering has warped my vision. I am praying to the Creator to help me be more compassionate.

I am not sure this is a question of compassion, or do we need to set the bar high? Will we be fair if we lower our standards? I can bend a little bit to accommodate your concerns. Maybe I was a bit too tough. Under my standards very few of us—and probably not me—would make it into the next world.

When I became course director for the dental students at Stony Brook, I lowered the bar for grades achieved on examinations. An "A" grade ranged from 87.5 to 100, instead of starting at 90. A "B" grade ranged from 77.5 to 87.5. A "C" ranged from 65 to 77.5, and less than 65 was a failure. Under the plan I just discussed, only those who achieved an "A" grade would be eligible to enter the Messianic Age.

If those who had a "B" grade were permitted admission, would that satisfy all of you? What this reasoning implies is that we are permitting imperfection on 22.5 percent of our moral choices. For the remaining 77.5 percent of our lifetime, we must achieve moral perfection. I don't know what this will translate to in terms of percentage of the world population, but we know from Scriptures that not everyone will be admitted into the Messianic

Age. Possibly, G-d will assign different quantitative values for each sin and each kind deed so that the actual percentage of 77.5 may still be equivalent to the percentage of time you have chosen good over evil. For example, if you commit a robbery, then it may take a lot of smaller good deeds on your part to make up for one large bad deed. Committing murder would likely disqualify you. I'm getting too complicated. We have to defer to G-d. He is the keeper of the scorecard.

The seven Princes nodded in agreement. Then they spoke.

Seven Princes: We will recommend your plan to the Creator, as we have done for the candidates who have preceded you. How would you level the playing field and make the process fair so that everyone is aware of your "B" plan?

*Yoseph:* In the ideal setting, I should be enormously wealthy, so I could start a mass marketing campaign to make everyone aware of the stakes. Abraham achieved success this way, but it's a different world today. The Internet, which was not available to any of you, would be the best way of spreading the information worldwide. However, who would believe me, unless I was wealthy?

With your permission, I would like to write a book on the Messiah Interviews. If the book becomes a success, the word would get out this way as well.

Notably, I don't think that we need to do anything. Everyone knows the difference between good and evil. The problem, as I said before, is choosing good over evil.

*Seth:* I take it from your last statement that you would favor letting things ride and leave the human race with the status quo. A kind of sink or swim attitude. Your wife Marcia's "paddle your own canoe" approach. Am I correct?

*Yoseph:* Correct. The old adage "you can lead a horse to water but you can't make it drink" still holds. I would re-emphasize one point. We still need to have a good and sincere heart, taking into consideration that we will, on perhaps many occasions, err, given the fallibility of our human nature.

Many people call themselves righteous or spiritual. Yet, they haven't invested their time and energy to do righteous deeds. We need to answer the call when people need us, and we need to give freely without expectations of a return benefit. Being a *mensch*, a good person, without any agenda scores points.

Often you will see holier than thou individuals preaching morality. Be on the lookout for such individuals, as their evil inclination is subtly hidden by their external trappings. The power of the evil inclination is so strong that ultimately it will show itself and the overly pious person will be unmasked. In the case of the Islamic terrorists, they do not hide behind their piety, blatantly displaying their evil inclination against innocent victims and every human ethical principle that G-d represents.

It's not easy for your good inclination, your *yetzer tov*, to overcome or subdue your *yetzer hara*, the evil inclination. The two are in a lifelong struggle, and the evil inclination bides its time, like the serpent in the Garden of Eden, to strike at any opportune moment. Recall that G-d tells Noah after the Flood that the imagery of man's heart is evil from his youth.

Just like bipolar disorder and other mental illnesses, you cannot will the evil inclination to disappear. Man does not have a genie to carry out such a wish, and often he may not want to because he enjoys the thrill of the ride to fame and fortune.

G-d sets up moral choices in our lives so that we have opportunities to defeat the evil inclination and be victorious. If the evil inclination beats you too many times in life, and sin prevails, you can reach the point where you no longer rule it. Rather, it rules you. Once that happens, it is probable that you have no other choice than to become anti-G-d. You have to justify and rationalize your sins, and it becomes harder and harder to find that *pintele yid* spark to ignite your Divine Soul.

I find the following biblical commentator's words profound. "Some people hate G-d. How can you hate a Deity that you don't believe in, in the first place?" I often wonder what sins scoffer atheists are hiding in their closets? I hope that they are aware that G-d sees right through them; yet, He is hoping that they have not completely extinguished their Divine sparks. Each time you battle the evil inclination and win with your good inclination, you weaken the power of the evil inclination. At one point, you will arrive at righteousness and make the evil inclination powerless. Because the spark remains inside their Divine Souls, even atheists can rejuvenate fire from the point of near extinction.

The evil inclination is your toughest enemy, as it is waging a battle for your Divine Soul. It begins on day one of your life, and its only interest is to make you stumble and fall. As Solomon says in his Book of Ecclesiastes, *Ecclesiastes 7:20: "For there is not a tzaddik on earth that does good and does not sin."* Even the most righteous person has sinned. Our *yetzer hara* is the internal voice, acting as a devil's advocate to push us in an amoral direction. The *yetzer hara* never gives up. A biblical commentator stated, "The greater the person, the greater the *yetzer hara*. But the *yetzer hara* is never greater than one's power to overcome it."

G-d's purpose in creating the evil inclination was that we defeat and best it. Free will is a gift to do just that. Unfortunately, for both G-d and us, the consequence of the gift of free will does not ensure that any of us will choose to love, trust, and be loyal to G-d and follow His Will and His Ways. Created in His image means that we try to function as Holy Beings in a spiritual sense. If our religion incorporates our spirituality, then our religion also becomes Holy.

The Jews were chosen to be Holy, to be a nation of Priests. We did not succeed, nor did any of humanity. G-d lives with man's choices and free will up to a point. No human has His patience. However, remember Senator Bradley's basketball analogy in his bid for the presidency of the United States: "You can only take so many elbows." G-d can turn off the faucet of this world at any time, just as instantaneously as He turned the spigot on prior to the Big Bang to create the universe.

The human race is the master of self-deception. Man is his own worst enemy. He uses his primal defense systems to rationalize away any situation where he feels uncomfortable admitting his mistakes and faults. His dander rises to the point where he pursues a course of action or maintains his stance, especially when he knows he is wrong. He rarely can ever accept blame himself when challenged, so it's easier to blame someone or something else—whatever is in vogue on that particular day.

*Seth:* I would like to change the subject for a moment. My weary bones are exhausted by the wordiness of your discussion, although I admit that I have been enlightened. What do you have to say, Yoseph, about chance and coincidence?

*Yoseph:* Marcia has always told me I'm long-winded. I'll try to be brief. Chance is for people who have not found G-d. Finding G-d means discovering life. G-d allows less-than-hardy believers to live their lives in this world under the random ups and downs of everyday existence, the normal vicissitudes of life. In contrast, for a spiritual human being who calls on his Divine Soul to charter his course through life, there are no coincidences. He employs his free will to carry out his daily goals and the challenges G-d throws his way, but it is G-d who determines the final outcome of his events.

*Seth:* I'd like to come full circle. How does my father's fate tie into the Messianic Age?

*Yoseph:* Your question will require a longer response. Your father represents the beginning point of G-d's plan for human-kind. After he and your mother disappointed G-d, it was the first moment of shame in our world. The harmony that existed between their bodies and souls, prior to their sin of desire and greed in the Garden of Eden, had been severed. Sin now was an integral part of their being, and it did not arise from some external serpent force. Adam and Eve didn't grow up in an immoral environment, which might be a pretext for their sin. They had no secular upbringing, nor were heredity and past experiences an excuse for their behavior.

G-d knew what was best for humans, yet man's nature is to desire more and not be grateful and content with what he has. Man became a creature of sensual pleasures after partaking of the forbidden fruit. He could no longer keep his penis in his pocket, despite G-d's later attempt to repair the damage of the Garden of Eden. Two thousand years after Adam and Eve, G-d's Covenant of Circumcision with Abraham was, in part, instituted to make man aware of the dangers of sexual promiscuity. History has proven the weakness of man's character time and time again. Man lusts for what he already has in his own backyard.

In my respectful view, Adam and Eve and the original sin were all part of destiny. G-d purposefully created good and evil, the righteous and wicked. I believe that G-d, in His infinite wisdom, brought evil in to the Garden of Eden because it is essential that we know evil to appreciate good—know imperfection to appreciate the perfection of the Messianic Age to come.

Therefore, there was really no choice for Adam and Eve. G-d led them in the direction of their desires, before free will existed. It is important to remember that G-d, and not Satan, grants free will. Satan, the serpent, only provided the means to G-d's intended end. Satan, too, is a creation of G-d. He serves G-d only at G-d's pleasure. G-d used an evil Satan to introduce free will, and what Satan represents, the evil inclination, will be destroyed at the End of Days.

At the End of Days, all of the Satans of this world, Satan's descendants, will be resurrected to face G-d's Judgment. There is a story about the Roman general, Titus, who burned down the Second Temple. He asked that he be cremated and that his ashes be scattered in different seas so that the Hebrew G-d could not find Him. You can run from G-d, but you can't hide from Him. Titus, like the evil and demonic villains of world history, will be given a second opportunity to be on the public stage. Their notoriety will not be for the purpose of re-enacting their roles as ruthless, conscious-less terrorists. As Daniel said, they will be resurrected to be held accountable and receive well-deserved, horrific, unimaginable punishment for their deeds. G-d's miracles will shine at the End of Days. So will His wrath and fury.

Our Creator would never leave humankind in a lurch, swinging from the rafters. Before Creation, G-d already had constructed a failsafe plan, and this, of course, is the Messianic Age. No matter the destruction of this world, whenever it comes by whatever means, it is all a prelude to the symphony of the next world. As Master Scientist, G-d has conducted the greatest scientific experiment of all time. Its truism cannot be duplicated by Nobel Laureates. Scientific Double Blind Studies are not necessary. The Messianic Age is the ultimate purpose of the Creation and evolution of humans.

*King David:* All of us in this Holy chamber have been waiting for the Redemption, when finally darkness will be transformed into Light. However, a new Garden of Eden will not erase the suffering of the righteous in our present world nor will it awaken the wicked to their senses to repent. Indeed, your proposed book about the Messiah Interviews may be of miniscule help and may also be irrelevant to this ageless problem of the wicked and the suffering. My question to you is do you think that the righteous will care about whether the evil are punished in the next world? Do you have an opinion?

*Yoseph:* Yes, I seem to have many opinions. Suffering is a bitter pill to swallow, especially when you see the wicked thriving around you. Speaking for myself, I will be able to let go of my suffering in the Messianic Age. I already have in this world. That may not be true for everyone who harbors horrific scars. So many have witnessed, firsthand, the actions of the wicked, who gloat while murdering them and declare that there is no G-d right in front of them. Resurrected Holocaust victims may want their pound of flesh.

From a strictly moral view, the evil need to be punished. There will be others, like myself, who will be so happy to be living in the Messianic Age that we could forgo further justice, condemnation, and purgatory. The wicked will have no place in the World to Come, and that will be satisfaction enough for us.

The Messiah is supposed to be a man of peace, and I plan to be that person who flies that banner. If destiny necessitates G-d's Judgment, so be it. The peace will then commence after justice is served.

*King David:* What will you do tonight, Yoseph? It's the Sabbath.

*Yoseph:* I'm going to begin to pray on a regular basis. Tonight I shall pray for all of humankind and for strength and compassion if I am chosen to be the Messiah. I shall also pray for G-d to help me eliminate my neurosis as quickly as possible so that I can be ready for a leadership role, if that is my destiny.

I want also for the first time to celebrate the Sabbath. I want to honor G-d's Creation by remembering the Sabbath. I've passed all my Saturdays without doing that.

*King David:* We shall adjourn until after the Sabbath, until Sunday morning. Shabbat Shalom everyone.

I began the walk home, my head buzzing with the now past memories of our discussions. Michael offered to walk with me, but I suggested to my friend that he needed his rest. I vowed to write everything down for my book, the *Messiah Interviews*. Life was good. I started to sing *Over the Rainbow*. Marcia was waiting.

# 16

# SABBATH LIGHTS

*M*ARCIA WAS WEARING HER double-heart, crown diamond necklace. We had been fortunate to obtain this magnificent, custom piece of jewelry, at a great price at a New York auction, in the fall of 1995.

I was just coming out of my bipolar-agitated clinical depression. After months of agony, I still don't know how I got better. Guaranteed, it wasn't due to any medication my psychiatrist had prescribed, because antidepressant pills and electroshock treatments had failed me miserably. There was no discernable explanation for my recovery. I had been through a desperately rough year, and I was lucky to be alive. I was only inches away from being dead from my suicide attempt. Had it not been for the miracle of the Creator coming to Marcia, I would have returned to the dust, from whence I came.

The bluish glow of the Sabbath candles, which Marcia lit that March 2008 Friday night in heaven, reminded me once again of the blue light miracle I experienced eight years earlier.

In my book, *Divinely Inspired*, I discussed Spiritual Lights. The first time I saw bright rays of blue light was in the summer of 2000, on our return car trip from Florida to New York. We had left Boynton Beach at midnight, having placed a bid to purchase our present Florida home. Eight hours into our drive, we were in Georgia, outside Savannah, when it happened. I was in the passenger seat. Out of the corner of my eye, I saw a ray of blue light coming from the sun onto the front window of the car. I couldn't believe what my eyes were seeing. I said nothing to Marcia at the time. I was too stunned for words. The next time that I saw the spiritual lights was two weeks later on my first day back at Stony Brook University, after a five-year, long-term disability leave. This time, I saw the blue ray sandwiched between two white rays. A month later, the picture was reversed, and a ray of white light was being emitted from the sun between two blue rays.

From slide presentations I had given in the classroom and at scientific research meetings, I used a blue background in my delivery. Blue is easy and relaxing on the eyes. There was no doubt that heaven's bluish tint appealed to my senses. There was an indescribable beauty of the heavenly blueness of the daylight, which blended into the multicolored tones of the Temple Mount. I couldn't help thinking, once more, that Judgment Day would be a day of blue. There would be neither day nor night, as prophesied in the Bible.

Coincidentally, Marcia's dress for the Shabbat was also blue. I hurried into the shower and then dressed for dinner. Lo and behold, in the closet was my blue striped shirt, which had once had black stripes. More unexplained miracles! The table setting was beautiful. There were slender blue and white candles in sterling silver candelabra. Orange blossom roses and creamy white orchids blew their delectable fragrance into our nostrils. Marcia told me that Elijah the prophet had delivered one of the Sanctuary's freshly baked Holy *Challah* Showbreads for our meal. I felt truly honored, as the Holy bread was reserved for the Third Temple priests.

We made the blessings over the Sabbath candles, red wine, and bread, and we sat down to eat a delicious meal of freshly cooked free-range chicken with roasted potatoes and green beans. Our appetizer was chopped eggs and onions, just like the way my grandmother, Rosie, would prepare for the Shabbat. For dessert, I ate no-sugar-added apple strudel while we drank heaven's nondairy equivalent to Bailey's Irish Cream with our decaffeinated coffee. There were more stars in the sky than I had ever seen, perhaps as brilliant and populated as the grains of the desert sands of the earth. Life couldn't get any better.

The next day, we went to the Outer Courtyard of the Temple for a service. The service would be led by the High Priest. We were met by Michael, who gave us a brief lesson in biblical history.

Moses' older brother, Aaron, had been chosen by G-d to start a separate branch of priests from the Levites. They were known as the *kohanim*. Aaron's two sons, Nadav and Avihu, had been consumed in the Sinai Desert when they had offered their *strange* incense fire to G-d in the Holy of Holies. G-d had used His own fire to take them. The boys couldn't contain themselves, as their souls were aflame to leave their bodies and be with their Creator. They unfortunately expired.

It was Aaron's two remaining sons, Elazar and Ithamar, who fathered twenty-four grandsons—the twenty-four *kohanim* families who would alternate on a weekly basis in the Temple service. For more than a thousand years, the High Priests were given the privilege to serve G-d. Twenty-three of the twenty-four families had corrupted this honor, and only one family remained steadfast, dedicated, and loyal to their intended spiritual role. Standing before us in the Inner Courtyard was Tzaddok himself, who had been the High Priest in Solomon's First Temple, approximately five hundred years after the Exodus from Egypt and the forty years of wondering in Sinai. The ancestral family of Tzaddok descended from one of the twenty-four grandsons, who had remained true and tried to the Creator. Thus, G-d had commanded that only a *kohanim* descendant of Tzaddok would serve as High Priest, when the Third Temple will be created on earth by the Messiah at the End of Days.

Michael went on to tell us that there had been numerous High Priests from the time of Aaron, until the destruction of the Second Temple by the Romans. Although it was forbidden, some of the kings of Israel falsely claimed dual status as both king and priest. On Yom Kippur, the Holy day of Repentance for the Jewish people, the High Priest visited the Holy of Holies and the Ark of the Covenant. It is said that the Temple priests tied a rope around the High Priest to drag him out dead, if G-d judged him to have disgraced himself and the people, by violating the slightest nuance of his obligation to fulfill the Ten Commandments.

Tzaddok was wearing the *techeilet* sky-blue woolen coat of the High Priest. The robe sported seventy-two golden wool bells alternating with seventy-two pomegranates attached at the hem. The hem was woven of blue, purple, and scarlet wool. Michael explained that the *techeilet* blue color, for dyeing the wool, was extracted from a now extinct tiny *chilazon* reptile found in Israel during biblical times.

Strapped over the robe, almost like a shield of armor, was the priestly breastplate. There were twelve colored earthly stones embedded octagonally in the breastplate, four sets of three running horizontally and three sets of four vertically. The stones were attached with golden thread. The breastplate itself was woven of linen and gold, sky-blue, dark-red, and crimson dyed wools. The stones of the breastplate were set in a golden rim setting, and the Hebrew writing depicted the names of Jacob's sons and grandsons, the Twelve Tribes of Israel—Asher, Dan, Naphtali, Reuben, Simeon, Judah, Issachar, Zebulon, Benjamin, Ephraim, and Manasseh. The breastplate was an integral part of the *ephod*, which resembled a tank top torn in front by the upper chest, so that this region of the High Priest's body divulged the top part of his blue robe.

There were two sardonyx stones sewn into the shoulders of the *ephod*, which were to serve as a remembrance for the Children of Israel. The remembrance stones had golden chains extending to golden hooks in the rings of the breastplate, so that the breastplate would remain fixed to the ephod. Tzaddok was gray-bearded and wore a white yarmulke on his head. His eyes bore the same blue hue as his robe, and they spoke to his humility and kindness.

The breastplate hosted the *Urim V'Tummim*, the mystical Divine name of G-d, which was written on a piece of parchment and placed by Moses into a flap of Aaron's *ephod* garment. The Name was called upon for Divine guidance whenever important questions were elicited from the High Priest. The High Priest's answers were mystically illuminated by G-d from the shining of specific letters on the stones, which contained the names of the Twelve Tribes. The letters formed words and the words formed sentences, as G-d responded through His High Priest.

As I sat gazing at Tzaddok's breastplate, I couldn't help thinking that possibly the magic of the *Urim V'Tummim* was the way we would ultimately identify Jews, as to which of the Twelve Tribes they belong to at the End of Days. According to Scriptures, Jews are to be ingathered by G-d to the Land of Israel, which will be divided up into twelve equal tribal parcels, and a thirteenth parcel for the Messiah. The Messiah's portion would house the Third Temple, an enlarged Temple Mount, and the housing quarters of the Levites and *kohanim* priests.

In my understanding of the Redemption, the Messianic Age would not terminate rabbinical Judaism, but it would end the stranglehold of the rabbis, acting as separatists among the Jewish population. Division of the Jews by secularity or differing religious beliefs would disappear and be replaced by a renewed spiritual covenant between G-d and man. In the new allocation of the land, individuals would be free to practice their religious beliefs, as long as they upheld unity and followed the Ten Commandments. This unity would be bolstered by Jewish attendance at the Third Temple on the holidays of Passover, Shavuous, and Sukkos. Rich or poor, all Jews become equal before their Creator when they enter the gates of the Temple.

In modern times, Jews are mainly represented by the Judean Tribes of Judah and Benjamin, and the Levite and *kohen* Priests. Approximately, 130 years before the destruction of Solomon's First Temple by the Babylonians, the Ten Northern Tribes were destroyed and exiled by the Assyrians. We refer to the Ten Northern Tribes as the Lost Tribes of Israel, It is thought that when Ezra and Nehemiah led the return of a small percentage of the exiled Babylonian Jews to Israel to build the Second Temple that there may have been members of the Ten Northern Tribes who also returned to help in the construction. Today, the Lost Tribes are Jews living their lives, unknowingly, as non-Jews. The United Israel movement cites many scriptural passages that indicate that the great majority of these non-Jews are, in fact, Protestants and Evangelical Christians. Their countries of origin are Germany, England, Scandinavia, and America.

I asked Michael about whether he thought animal sacrifices would continue in the future Third Temple on earth. His reply was not entirely helpful. He said that there was no need for such sacrifices in heaven, because all who were here walked with G-d. He then turned the tables on me and asked me what I thought. I said that I was dead set against sacrifices but that I would keep the sacrificial altar for ancient historical purposes if I were chosen as the Messiah.

Michael asked me to elaborate, for he knew full well, as did I, that there would be strong opposition to disbanding sacrifices. What about the Red Heifer, he queried? I replied that both sacrifices and the red heifer should be remembered as symbolic to the plight of the Jews in their struggle for a lasting spirituality within themselves.

In biblical times, when animals were sacrificed in the Temple, the sinner bringing the sacrifice was supposed to see himself being burned on the altar, instead of the animal he gave up for slaughter to the Temple priests. There was no psychology or Primal Therapy back then, so this was G-d's way of keeping man keenly aware of his human mistakes. Man could repent in this way and hopefully depart the Temple that day, ready to take up the challenges of life with renewed and elevated commitment to the Ten Commandments and to his Creator. The Jews continued to lose their way and G-d commented on the dilemma of humankind by expressing His annoyance, sarcasm, or frustration when He said, *"What good are your sacrifices if you cannot follow my Commandments?"* There is the thought that we would still bring non-animal thanksgiving *sacrifices*, but I look at these as praising and honoring the Creator.

I must have been daydreaming, because Tzaddok had completed his sermon. His topic centered around life being a juggernaut that could be conquered if one has faith and trust in G-d. He was looking forward to the Messianic Age, when one of his earthly descendants would assume the role of High Priest and deliver a similar speech at the time of the future Third Temple on earth. He looked straight into my eyes and said, "Yoseph, the Redemption is not about any of us, and it's about all of us. We shall be passenger pigeons carrying the message of His Will at the End of Days—a message that finally will revolutionize humankind and bring cleansing and purity to the world. The Messiah will lead G-d's charge."

I wondered when G-d would signal the beginning of the end. Would I still be alive? I was 66, and that did not leave much time.

Doubts surfaced. My only solace was the Prophet Isaiah's statement in *Isaiah 42:4, "He (the Messiah) shall not fail or be crushed until he sets right in the world."* I decided to let it go, as I had no control over G-d's choice for the Messiah.

That night, Marcia and I re-watched Cecil B. DeMille's epic movie *The Ten Commandments*. I thought I would face Moses tomorrow morning. I was wrong. It was King David. I had no idea what to expect, and judging from my recent experiences with the seven Princes, I was sure to encounter surprises. I vowed to myself to carry over the joy and appreciation I was feeling to tomorrow's interview. I hoped that I would be as animated and free as I felt right in the now of the moment. Life was indeed good.

17

# KING DAVID

*CENTURIES AGO, DURING* the Exodus, G-d spoke to Moses with the following words: *"I will have mercy and kindness to whomever I desire, even to a sinner who does not deserve Divine mercy."* I am that sinner.

*King David:* Good morning to all. Yoseph, you probably have guessed my first question, which is close to my heart. Why should you be the Redeemer? You, like me, were a sinner.

*Yoseph:* We are all sinners, King David. G-d made us imperfect when He gave us the gift of Free Will. Luckily, His compassion and benevolence toward us allowed us a second gift: repentance. The sages record that G-d knew that He needed repentance for human flesh, even before He created us and the universe.

*King David:* We can't just be forgiven outright for our sins. In addition to the Day of Judgment in the World to Come, we need to learn lessons in the present world. Can you comment? I deserved to be punished for my sins, and I was, but what is the *take home message*?

*Yoseph:* From biblical history, we know that whenever He so chooses, G-d communicates with individuals who have the potential to reach elevated spiritual heights. All of you are a testament to righteousness, despite your personal sins. In a similar vein, G-d teaches us lessons of accountability.

These lessons are not for the everyday Joe who lives his life without attention to spiritual meaning. They are reserved only for His righteous people. The take home message is that G-d acts *Measure for Measure.*

The consequences for Adam and Eve were that they had to leave the very same magnificent Garden of Eden that they had corrupted with their sin. You were sickly smitten with the love of Bat Sheba, and your sin was to spend many years of your relatively short life of seventy years being ill. Jacob favored Joseph, and he lost the favor of his other sons, who almost destroyed Joseph. Abraham lost Sarah, the love of his life because he was willing to hurt his loving son, Isaac. Moses was held to the highest standard, and when he violated his leadership powers, G-d chose to deny him his most powerful desire: the Promised Land. We all have been subject to the Creator's acts of measure for measure. Our saying "we are sorry" does not wipe the slate clean. In Primal Therapy, you wipe out the pain of the memory, but the memory remains. Sins can be expunged by the gut-wrenching repentance of the sinner, but repentance doesn't wipe out the sin itself.

I cheated in science, and it was science that brought me down to a refractive depression and an almost fatal suicide attempt. I had hit bottom and was forced, in shame and disgrace, to leave the university for five years.

If we recognize His goodness, we can also observe that measure for measure is applicable to the rewards that G-d metes out in this world. I suffered for many years with neurosis, migraines, and bipolar disorder because my parents couldn't or didn't know how to offer me true love. My reward for embarking on the spiritual path is Marcia, the greatest gift of love anyone could hope to have. I grew up in a house where I had no space of my own. Today, I have been blessed with a most spacious, beautiful home. I feel so much gratitude that the Almighty has entered my life and chosen to shine His *Shechinah* upon me.

*King David:* You speak a lot about sincerity of the heart. What else do you have in your character arsenal that would win us over to your side?

*Yoseph:* I have integrity. I hope I won't compromise my moral principles. I will follow the Ten Commandments, and I will stand strong and tall yet be merciful and compassionate. I understand that being the Messiah is not about me. Once king, you governed, for the most part, for the benefit of the Israeli people and not for your own personal interests. I shall do likewise.

I have had much suffering in my life, and I believe I can identify with those whose drudgery has brought them to their wits end. I can be that beacon of light and hope. With each passing day, I grow stronger spiritually. I know that I have goodness and kindness in my heart. Like Jesus, I will lift up the needy out of the dunghill and be that wise man who seeks counsel from others in my kingdom. Solomon says that a wise man seeks counsel, and I shall follow his wisdom. There will be no manipulation on my part, and I will expect the same out of my subjects. My motto shall be that nobody has the right to hurt you.

I believe that my leadership skills are untapped. A Messianic king will start with a stacked deck in his favor. There will be food, shelter, and clothing for all, and no poverty. However, the cards can quickly sour, as we have seen with the Israelites, who couldn't maintain the wonders of Sinai. That won't happen on my watch. Each one of us shall be accountable for our actions, and the punishment shall fit the crime, although with the Evil Inclination subdued, it's hard to imagine crimes of immorality.

Above all, my devotion and loyalty will be to my Creator, and I will live the words, "to be created in His image."

*King David:* It took me seven years past my anointment as king to unite the Twelve Tribes behind my throne. Given the modern world, you have an essentially impossible task. How can you achieve your goals?

*Yoseph:* You are absolutely right. My task will be daunting. I not only have to unite the Jews; I also have to convince the world, too. You know as well as I that whenever a Redeemer steps forth to do good in this world he or she will be singled out to be cut off at the knees. No one wants to give up one inch of their turf, and when you threaten them by taking the high ground, they find all kinds of reasons to take pot shots at you and make every effort to gun you down. Such individuals are governed by badness of their animal souls.

*King David:* My son, Solomon, used to say, *"There is nothing new under the sun."* You speak eloquently; however, what I'm hearing from you is not original. I've heard it before. Show me something that makes you uniquely suitable to be the Messiah. Your Divine miracles are not extraordinary nor do they provide definitive evidence that they are connected to your asserted mission of seeking this divine role. Your character qualities and intelligence are fairly good, but they are not exceptional. Your knowledge of biblical history is adequate, though you are not a Torah scholar. You write well, yet, so do a whole lot of others, who could easily match your skills and qualify to be the Messiah. Your spiritual words have not been matched by spiritual deeds in life. And finally, and most important, the Ancient One has never asked you to be the Messiah. You have sought this esteemed position entirely on your own.

I had been anticipating the bombshell. I just didn't see this explosion coming. We had started off the morning so pleasantly that I was lulled into a feeling of false ease about the interview. Now, for the first time, I did not have an adequate answer for a question. All escape routes had been sealed by King David.

According to Kabbalah wisdom, the solution is there before the problem, and according to Einstein, the problem cannot be solved at the same level where the problem was created. My problem was that the problem was being asked at the human level, when the answer demanded a Divine response. I wished I were an angel, or at least a prophet with a claim to Divinity.

Where was G-d when I needed Him? King David had negated all my previous arguments. The whole interview process had been for naught. I was stuck, or it seemed so, as panic was making its move to gain a foothold in my body. As I reflected anxiously and strenuously, with all eyes glued on me, I considered that David's question might be a trap. Is it humanly possible to answer all questions when only G-d has the Divine Wisdom to do so?

*"Do not be wise in your eyes,"* said Solomon. One cannot be too smart. The Evil Inclination is not only sly and subtle in an overly

pious preacher, but also it secretly exists in individuals who claim to be assholes in smarty-pants.

I thought of Richard Gere's line in the movie An *Officer and a Gentleman*: "I don't have anywhere else to go." It was time to answer the king.

*Yoseph:* All of your reasons, at first glance, King David, are correct, but the whole is often greater than the sum of its parts. Officially, I have not been invited by G-d to be His Messiah. I am answering a Divine call within myself to give back to the Creator for the blessings and miracles He has bestowed upon me. What service is higher than being a king, as you well know?

Never in my life have I wished to soar with angels as I do now. I am certainly not naïve to think that I can pull this off alone. The wise man seeks counsel—the Princes' expert advice, the celestial assistance of angelic forces, and the wisdom of the Hebrew prophets. In the Book of Job, *Iyov 32:7,* Job said it best: *"Days speak, and a multitude of years teach wisdom."* Your experiences will be invaluable. Most of all though, I need G-d's infinite, Divine Wisdom and guidance at my side.

The answer to your question cannot come from a human mouth. We will need G-d to weigh in and decide if I am worthy to be the Messiah. G-d has bet on underdogs before, King David.

King David smiled in my reference to him and Goliath, and to G-d choosing him, a shepherd boy, to be king of Israel.

*Yoseph:* Moreover, G-d already knows who the Messiah is, because his name was known to Him before Creation. As Maimonides elegantly states, "He is the knower, the known, and the knowledge." Also, as the Book of Isaiah, *Isaiah 55:9,* emphatically teaches, *"As the heavens are higher than earth, so are My ways higher than your ways, and My thoughts are higher than your thoughts."*

I quote a biblical commentator: "Greatness is not reserved for the great. The great are simply those who have risen to meet their destiny." Destiny is at work here, and no earthly human, past or present, knows who the Messiah will be. G-d's flame is burning inside me, and I am prepared right now to spread His Light to His children. I think we should see this interview process through, and let it run its course. I am not ready to cash my chips in. Neither should this advisory council. Let's see what stuff I'm made of.

If I'm not chosen as the Messiah, I, of course, will be disappointed. However, there is still life to live in this world, after meeting all of you in heaven. The memories of the Messiah Interviews have already been quite remarkable. I can't thank you and heaven enough.

*King David:* As chairperson of this committee, I think I can speak for all of us. Yoseph, you are growing as a candidate. We all agree that we should withhold further comments about your suitability to be the Messiah until the process has been completed and we get to know you thoroughly. This doesn't mean that our questions will get any easier. We have given our solemn oath to the Almighty to find His Messiah, even though He already knows who that is. If we don't approve, He won't overrule us. The stakes are too high. Now, we continue the interview.

You seem to have the potential for greatness. Is that enough?

*Yoseph:* No. My desire has to be powerful, but my passion has to be channeled in the right direction. No question, greatness elevates you, and having your soul unify with G-d is magical. However, the right course is for your soul to stay put on earth and do its work for humanity. You must adopt the physician's oath, "Do no harm." This is especially true as you ascend the spiritual ladder, and it is unquestionably required for a future king of the golden days ahead.

My soul, like yours King David, has dripped from the agony of suffering (*Psalms 119:28*). This has stood me well in my life, and I can truly appreciate a Messianic Age of joy. You say in your writings in the Book of Psalms, *Psalms 126:5, "Those who sow in tears shall reap in joy."* I used to be a pessimist, but now I'm an optimist, thanks to the Divine Providence of the Creator. I see the potential for the cup overflowing.

*King David:* If you are faced with a tough or easy choice, which will you choose? And what about when all the choices are bad?

*Yoseph:* I'll decide based upon what is morally the right action, not the measure of ease or difficulty. When the choices are all bad, I will call upon G-d, because I don't want to make the least stressful choice, since there will still be harm to some.

*King David:* My ancestor, Judah, would have answered the way you did. Do you know how he responded?

*Yoseph:* Yes, he publicly admitted his drunken affair with Tamar, although his honesty may have cost him dearly. He could have taken an easier way out, without the potential to self-destruct. Then when Joseph imprisoned their brother, Benjamin, Judah pleaded on behalf of his aging father, Jacob. Judah asked Joseph to take him as prisoner, instead of his youngest brother Benjamin, whom Jacob loved greatly. Benjamin was the only son still alive from his true love, Rachel.

Judah spoke from his heart and his words entered Joseph's heart. Jacob had long believed that his and Rachel's other son, Joseph, was dead. Judah was far from perfect, as he had been part of his brothers' plot to kill Joseph. By Judah's actions, the Tribe of Judah was blessed by Jacob to be the one among the Twelve Tribes from whom the Messiah will come.

*King David:* How will you get your subjects to look up to you and respect you?

*Yoseph:* By being honest and humble. Half the battle has been won, as we are selecting the cream of the crop to enter the Messianic Age. We shouldn't be so naïve to think that there won't be problems. My plan calls for admitting individuals with an 80 percent or "B" morality, and we know from past experience and human nature that the best of individuals stray.

I shall be the heart of the nation. All the hearts of my subjects will beat separately on their own, and the rhythm of my heart will have to synchronize with each of their hearts. I shall be the conductor of my subjects, who will act as musicians and bring harmony to our new world. I shall set the spiritual pace and tone for the Messianic nation and embody within myself all that is good in G-d's Eyes. Once I set the standards and values, I shall more or less be able to govern the nation on automatic pilot.

As Ronald Reagan said, "A great leader is not necessarily one who does great things but one who inspires others to do great things." Great leaders often come from humble and troubled beginnings, while greatness often begins from unnoticed events in the life of an individual. Who would have ever thought that an unexceptional movie actor could become an exceptional leader and inspire a nation through his oratory and optimism?

The Talmud states that for he who pursues greatness, the greatness eludes him. And those who avoid greatness are sought by greatness. Au contraire, I guess I am pursing greatness. There is a part of my path that is self, and a part that is selfless and Divinely altruistic. G-d knows the intentions behind my actions. I can't change who I am, as all my experiences are a part of me. I do speak out about past right and wrong, because I have chosen right over wrong. I do have faults, but I have accepted myself with all my shortcomings. If G-d wants me, He will have to accept me as I am today. I can't pretend to be anyone else. As the quote goes, "What you see is what you get."

*King David:* We'll take a thirty-minute break and resume at 11 a.m. with Moses leading our discussion.

*Michael:* Come on, Yoseph. Let's go out for a breath of fresh air to clear your mind. We can pick up a natural blended fruit drink just outside the Temple Mount.

I followed Michael out of the Temple, and we headed north. The Third Temple was not centrally located within the Temple Mount, as it was closest to the northern wall.

I couldn't help but think that I had blown the interview with King David. At the very best, I clawed my way back to a draw. What I did do, however, was to secure a promise that we would see the Messiah Interviews through to completion.

*Michael:* You seem troubled. Let me assure you that although you were not stupendous, you did do much better than average. I would rate your performance as a high "B," and that says a lot, especially in the difficult climate you have been performing in. None of the Princes are slouches. They were selected by G-d, Himself, because they represent intelligence beyond your earthly peers. They may not seem to act fairly to you, but I can assure you that they are among the most honorable men of humanity.

*Yoseph:* You're, of course, right Michael. They are only doing their job. I can't hope to gain their respect at this point. It's just that I'm used to getting grades of "A" on examinations. It brings up past feelings of not being wanted and inferiority.

Once outside, we were treated to another blissful day in heaven. Although I felt revved up, there was tranquility in the air. For the life of me, I don't know why I recalled an international research meeting in 1984 in Belgium, where Marcia and I met a Sexologist by the name of Dick. He would periodically remark in monotone and smirking seriousness, "There's a heaviness in here. Don't you feel it?" The memory of Dick brought a much-needed laugh to my psyche.

Michael and I finished our mix of a delicious pineapple, papaya, kiwi fruit drink and headed back inside. My choice was to cut and run, or charge ahead like the Light Brigade. I was not a soldier in the Civil War, fighting in hand-to-hand combat. Yet, the Messiah Interviews seemed just like that on a mental level.

I thought back to my mania where I was playing chess with Saddam Hussein, strategizing to vanquish him in the Gulf War. The irony was that I didn't play chess.

My Tai Chi instructor had used the Taoist term *Sat Sung*, which means "meeting of truth." To get to the truth was an excruciating experience, and how many times can one get the wind knocked out of his sails? As many times as it takes, I guess, until the boat capsizes.

# 18

# MOSES

*T*HE SEVEN PRINCES WERE joking with each other when we arrived back in the Sanctuary. I didn't realize that they were laughing about the sexologist. How could there be heaviness in heaven? I began to laugh with them. There was Moses, whose name means "to be drawn from the water." His biography, along with Jesus, may be the most famous in human history.

*Moses:* As King David has commanded, I shall not question your competence to lead the free world. I do, however, want to use my time to probe your mind. No human can know the intention of another's thoughts. Here in heaven, G-d has allowed us to read your thoughts, but only G-d knows your and everyone else's intentions.

My first question isn't really a question. I want you to discuss the concept of truth.

*Yoseph:* Oh Yah, this is going to be fun.

They all laughed. I had made a slip of the tongue. Maybe if I were a comedian, I could win their hearts over. Telling a joke was not my forte.

I tried to start out on familiar grounds with a commentator's quote from the Book of Job that I had cited in my book, *Divinely Inspired*:

*Yoseph:* "Truth is absolute only when we can divorce it from the person who proclaims it." Galileo's concept of a world that was circular, and not flat as believed at the time, fits this definition. So does Isaac Newton's insightful Gravity Theory or Einstein's Theory of Relativity. If you remove these scientists, their uniquely original concepts still stand.

In most cases, truth is not absolute, and it depends upon the mindset of the individual or group of individuals. The clarity of truth becomes clouded. In biology, it's a lot harder to make definitive statements about truth, because with new discoveries, new truths emerge. The bottom line is that absolute truth is dicey.

Is Evolution truth? In my opinion, yes, except that many scientific details are missing. Is Creation, truth? Absolutely, except that G-d has not been forthright in sharing His secrets of the universe. It will take the Creator to publicly reinvest Himself on the world stage to convince the skeptics and scoffers that He was and is the Father of both Evolution and Creation.

Do angels fly UFOs, as I suggested? I must admit that I don't know, as most people's logic cannot agree with the premise that the UFOs exist in the first place. Do miracles exist? There is no doubt in my mind, as I have personally experienced them. Yet, most people can explain away these unusual events by the forces of nature or by disbelieving entirely. Are their paranormal events in our world? An affirmative yes.

Will there be a Messianic Age, and does a Supreme Being who transcends time exist? Yes, for those who have made the leap of faith, but no, for those who choose to have no faith. Only G-d can set the record straight, and when He appears at the End of Days, the truth will be absolute, as we will be able to divorce the truth from He who proclaims it—our Creator.

*Moses:* Is Free Will a truth?

*Yoseph:* Yes, but it's not absolute. Atheists believe that free will is a product of human evolution. Animals act on instinct. The faithful believe free will is a gift from the Creator. In human history, free will was taken away through enforcement of slavery in society, dating back to biblical times. And sometimes our neurotic backgrounds lead us into victimized, non-free-will choices.

On the other hand, if you believe that free will is within the domain of the Creator, you might question the absolute validity of this free will one hundred percent of the time. Through His Omnipotence, G-d has the infinite power to interfere with free will, if He thinks the course of history needs changing or He requires it to be viewed by man with a different slant. During the time of the Exodus, G-d hardened the Pharaoh's heart so he would refuse to let the Jews go until the bitter end. Otherwise, after suffering the miracles of the plagues, the Pharaoh would have thrown in the towel. G-d did this to teach us a lesson in human history and to make an example of the cruelty of man toward man.

If we didn't have free will, we couldn't choose to believe in G-d with faith, or disbelieve in Him, or be agnostic, and sit on the fence. I often reflect on my own experiences and wonder if G-d has interfered with my free will.

*Moses:* What about the Omniscience of G-d? How do you reconcile that with free will?

*Yoseph:* Oh, you mean that our all-knowing G-d knows what we are going to do before we do it. Yes, I believe this. I also believe that G-d can be disappointed by our free will choices. When the first king of Israel, King Saul, chose not to obey G-d's Will, G-d was still hoping that Saul would use his free will to act as G-d desired.

At the last moment, our free will permits us to still change our minds. From moment to moment, G-d knows our thoughts, even when we finally decide on a course of action. We can even later change our minds. His Omniscience implies total knowledge of the thoughts and intentions of human beings at all times.

In the Book of Jeremiah, *Jeremiah 17:10,* we find the passage, *"I am G-d who examines the heart (of man) and inspects the recesses of the mind."* In Proverbs, Solomon speaks of the soul of man being the lamp of G-d with which He examines the inner parts. There is a belief in Judaism by some that the Divine Soul exists in the heart while others believe that the Soul is found in the brain. From Jeremiah, we learn that the Divine Soul may reside in both anatomical locations.

I think G-d is very sad, troubled, and disappointed in the human race. We continue to make a mess out of our gift of life, our earth, and our universe.

*Moses:* Do you have anything more to say about truth?

*Yoseph:* Yes, I can say a little more. I asserted earlier that our free will allows us to make moral and non-moral choices in life. I wanted to reiterate that for the righteous, those with the "A" and perhaps "B" moral averages, G-d determines the final outcome, success or failure, of their non-moral choices.

Not everyone falls into this category. Most people are subject to the randomness and whims of daily events.

Furthermore, only G-d knows the truth about the future. In biblical days, truth was expressed through the Hebrew prophets. In Messianic times, it is said that our children shall prophesy once again.

*Moses:* It would do us well to remember what Solomon said about truth.

*Yoseph: "True speech is established forever, but a false tongue is only for a moment."*

Solomon was saying that truth remains from the moment it is uttered. It cannot be altered, for if it is, it will not be truth and will change from moment to moment. Truths must be eternal. Without humility, I don't think you can discover truth. If your ego gets out in front of you, you may never find truth. In Primal Therapy, I have been able to strip away my defense system so I can now answer your questions with truth.

There are two Hebrew expressions for performing kind deeds. They also apply to truth. *Shelo lishma* means "to carry out the mitzvah or kind deed for one's own sake." However, it is better to operate on the principle of simply, *lishma*, meaning "for its own sake, without any strings or conditions."

Truth has to stand on its own and ought not be manipulated by us in the crevices of our minds. When we act with *lishma*, we are behaving in the Image of G-d. For those of us with Faith, we are doing it for the love of G-d and not for self. In truth, I am operating on both levels, *shelo lishma* and *lishma*. I hope that as I continue to grow spiritually and leave the burdens of my neurosis behind, I will be acting in my heart with more and more *lishma*.

*Emes,* or truth, also means "honesty and sincerity in your heart." To stand tall in G-d's demanding place, I need to be truthful, beyond the letter of the law.

*Moses:* Yoseph, do you know the difference between transgressions and iniquities?

*Yoseph:* No.

*Moses:* Transgressions are clear offenses, readily identified. Iniquities are more subtle. They are hidden from view in the intentions of your thoughts, which you may or may not exercise into action. No one can prevent thoughts of desire from entering our minds. The challenge is whether you act upon these insatiable thoughts with willful desire. I need to extract those subtle thoughts from you, if this body is to give our approval for you to become the Messiah. There must be unanimity among us for you to go forward to the future.

We will examine your iniquities starting right now. It's so important to do this, because a framework of honesty gets to the central core of the Jewish problem. These interviews are not about you. They are about Judaism and humankind. If you cannot be totally forthright in your answers, then there is no place for you here in heaven, or as G-d's Messiah.

The Almighty told the Jewish people long ago that He would hold them accountable for their iniquities, because He had chosen them among the nations to serve as His Spiritual Light to the world. Few Jews understand this concept, which has existed since the time of the declaration of the Ten Commandments at Mount Sinai.

In the larger scope, we as individual Jews are responsible for all Jews, no matter our geographical location and no matter when we live—past, present, or future. G-d has never broken His

Covenant with the Patriarchs, but He has drifted back to heaven, because of our continued transgressions and iniquities. He is present in our world, hither and there, offering His bounties to His righteous. However, He is no longer on the public stage, as He once was in biblical times. He ensures that the world will not collapse, but man has been on His own since his immoral actions led to the destruction of the First Temple.

The Holocaust is a horrible outcome and tragedy of our behavior throughout the ages. Demonic humans have spewed their hatred because man and the Jews, in particular, have not kept their part of the Covenant with the Creator. If we Jews had lined up behind G-d, belonged to G-d, then G-d would have come to humanity's aid as He did when the Jews conquered the land under Joshua. For seven years of war against the Canaanite idol-worshipping tribes, there were less than a handful of Jewish casualties. Can we say that in your time, Yoseph?

There have been more people with "C" and failing grades in their free will than there are individuals who are demonstrably more good than bad. The lines have been drawn in the sand. In Messianic times, the pendulum may or may not swing according to your theory. G-d did destroy the evil rabble-rousers of the Golden Calf, so your proposal that not all Jews will make it to the Messianic Age has merit. However, I stood with the majority of the Israelites and tried to refine their character during forty years of wondering in the desert. The big question of questions remains. Will we enter the New World in peace, or will we first have to go through bloody times at the End of Days?

Believe it or not, some of this depends on you, Yoseph, if you are granted the awesome responsibility of becoming the

Messiah. The Messiah needs to stand taller than anyone has stood before.

I gulped, and could not contain my anxiety. My iniquities? What hell is he leading me into?

I sat there in awe of this Holy man. There was no sign of his speech impediment. He was already in Messianic days, when healing would take place—when the eyes of the blind will be opened and the ears of the deaf will be unstopped, as Isaiah phrases it. Moses was inspiring, and today his comments, in my mind, would rank with Jesus' Sermon on the Mount and with the great speeches of history.

*Moses:* Yoseph, please recite the Ten Commandments from the Torah or from your own book, *Divinely Inspired.* I have a copy of it, which you can use. After each Commandment, I want you to dig deep into your iniquities.

It was my turn to laugh, and I did so. How did my book, which sold so few copies, wind up in heaven? This carnival atmosphere was better than an Oprah Winfrey recommendation.

I began the Ten Commandments. These seemingly simple words, spoken by G-d to the Israelites, more than 3,300 years ago at the Revelation of Sinai, have turned out to be the most difficult challenge of all.

In my mind, the most remarkable event recorded in human history was G-d's Voice coming out of the fire to deliver the Ten Commandments at Mount Sinai to a throng of hundreds of thousands.

The Israelites had the opportunity to soar with angels, and they did, but they could not sustain such elevated spiritual blessings.

*First Commandment:*

*I am God your Lord, Who brought you out of Egypt, from the place of slavery.*

184

*Yoseph:* There are no secrets in my brain. I am a believer.

Second Commandment:

*Do not have any other gods before Me.*

*Do not represent (such gods) by a statue or picture of anything in the heaven above, or the earth below, or in the water below the land. Do not bow down to (such gods) and do not worship them. I God your Lord am a God who demands exclusive worship, where my enemies are concerned. I keep in mind the sin of the fathers for (their) descendants for three and four (generations). But to those who love me, I show love for thousands (of generations).*

Third Commandment:

*Do not take the Name of God your Lord in Vain. God will not allow the person who takes His Name in vain to go unpunished.*

*Yoseph:* When the Ten Commandments were declared, there were no Christians, Muslims, Buddhists, Hindus, Taoists, etc. The Second Commandment applies only to past, present, and future generations of Jews. Nowhere in the Torah is there a reference to peoples other than the Jews. I strictly adhere to the Second Commandment.

Yes, I have taken the Name of the Lord in vain. Since G-d's entering my life with Divine Providence ten years ago, I have rarely done so.

Fourth Commandment:

*Observe the Sabbath to keep it Holy, as your Lord commanded you. You can work during the six weekdays, and do all your tasks, but Saturday is the Sabbath to God your Lord, so do not do anything that constitutes work. (This includes) your son, your daughter, your male and female slave, your ox, your donkey, your (other) animals, and the foreigner who is in your gate. Your male and female slaves will then be able to rest as you do. You must remember that you*

*were slaves in Egypt when God your Lord brought you out with
an outstretched arm. It is for this reason that God your Lord has
commanded you to keep the Sabbath.*

*Yoseph:* The sages remark that more than the Jews keep
the Sabbath—the Sabbath keeps the Jews. I freely admit that
I haven't kept the Sabbath. However, I reflect on G-d during
the Sabbath and every other day of the week.

There is another way to look at the Seven Days of Creation.
One day in seven to think about G-d is asking you to only
do this a maximum of 14 percent of your week. And during
this day of rest, you are not actually reflecting on G-d all of
the time, so that this percentage, in reality, is less than half.
Sundown to sundown, from Friday to Saturday, is G-d's choice
for the Jews. Sunday for Christians and Friday for Muslims
have become the days for their respective Holy days. My point
is, that it would be nice to express one's gratitude for the world
G-d gave us and for the gift of life, at least, at some time during
the course of the week. Many individuals go on for months,
and even years, without giving G-d a second thought.

<u>Fifth Commandment:</u>

*Honor your father and your mother, as God your Lord commanded
you.*

*Yoseph:* I could write volumes on this commandment.
The short and the sweet of it is that I treated my parents with
respect and loved them unconditionally.

The reverse was not true, unfortunately for me, as there
were countless occasions when they never returned my love.
My father tried, and he did care, but he was a victim of his
own neurosis, which blocked his ability to offer true love.
His love was not the real love that I give to my children. My

father's love centered on whether you were accomplished in sports, because this is what he treasured in his own life. I could never understand why I didn't receive his love when I became a professor at Stony Brook University. I once asked my brother, why? His reply, "Dad only loves sports."

My mother was narcissistic and was just not willing to share any part of herself to nurture and love her children. Narcissism implies that there is only room for self-love, the "me" syndrome. In our phone calls from New York to Toronto, my mother would say she loved me. However, love to her meant my feeding her insatiable narcissism by telling her that I loved her, too.

Several years ago, I asked my mother whether she was sorry for anything in her life. She thought for a moment, and shockingly replied, "No."

My parents really never saw me, never knew me. How very sad for me, as I have always personally identified with and felt the knife's sharp pain and the hurtful sting of Marlon Brando's famous words in the movie *On the Waterfront*: "I could ah been a contender, Charlie, instead of the bum who I am." My words would have been, "We could have been a family of love, mommy and daddy, instead of the virtual nothing that we were."

Sixth Commandment:

*Do not commit murder.*

Seventh Commandment:

*Do not commit adultery.*

*Yoseph:* "Stop right here, Yoseph," I thought to myself. This is a problem. The key word is *commit*, which means "to act." I have fully adhered to this commandment in forty years of two marriages. Yet, if a different bar or standard is set for the Messiah, then I can't high jump it, because I have committed adultery in my thoughts.

Moses said at the outset that he will be looking for the subtle desires of my heart in my hidden thoughts. The Messiah needs to be judged at a higher standard. Yet, that's impossible because man, no matter who the man is, will always be imperfect, at least, in this world. I don't know what will happen in the Messianic Age, but I suspect that un-acted upon desire will still be there.

Committing the act of adultery is morally wrong. Humans know this, as well as they know good from evil; yet, that doesn't seem to stop anyone. Our society offers innumerable enticements, which lead to transgressions. The Seventh Commandment is a judgment of G-d, and not of humans, because G-d knows that if we act immorally on our thoughts, we invariably hurt someone else. Most tests that G-d gives us are for the benefit of the individual, if he can make the right choice. Murder, adultery, and theft are societal tests.

If man is neither impotent nor erectile-challenged because of the side effects of medication, his natural tendency and need is to release his sperm from his penis. There is nothing in my life that is comparable to being touched by Marcia, except Marcia herself. G-d built our physical bodies this way, to give us untold pleasures. G-d placed our penis on a par with our heart and our brain, above other body organs, because He wanted to use the penis as one of His tests of morality.

Yes, I have looked and fantasized about other women, but the Ten Commandments bracelet on my wrist keeps me in check with respect to this commandment. I have strong sexual urges, or I used to have them. Age is taming them, although I don't at this point need Viagra. In fact, it's better for me to not take these erectile dysfunction drugs until I absolutely need them. I don't want to be tempted by my thoughts. I don't want to give into my iniquities.

I am also acutely aware that Marcia is the best thing that ever happened to me, and I wouldn't jeopardize our love for all the women in the world.

There was one point when I almost strayed about ten years ago in a New Age encounter, but it was not sexual, as Marcia thought. I make no excuse, but it was my neurotic need to feel special. I spoke about this in earlier interviews, but it's worth repeating. If you never have felt special with your parents, you continually and hopelessly search for admiration and validation. You search, even when it is right in front of you in your immediate environment. When I was highly neurotic, neither G-d nor Marcia could fill that bottomless pit to feel special. Now instead of the sexuality, I feel the sadness that I was not special during my time with my parents.

*Eighth Commandment:*

*Do not steal.*

*Yoseph:* There are different types of stealing. We all know robbery. Lack of honesty and abandonment of trust are also subtle forms of stealing. In *Divinely Inspired*, I wrote about my significant scientific cheating. I was dishonest with my mentors, and I violated their trust in me. Because of my dishonesty, a cancer continued to grow in me, until I could bear the pain no more. I made gut-wrenching confessions to Stony Brook and to my master's and doctoral degree mentors. All who I told had undeserved compassion for me. I can never wipe the slate clean. All I can do is go on with my life and wait to be judged at *Ya ha Din ha Gadol*, Judgment Day.

I took a deep breath, glanced over at Moses, and then my eyes looked downward. Moses was staring right through me, and I realized that this commandment could be my downfall. My Ten Commandment bracelet would not help me, as I had broken this commandment, and I had done it recently. I was ashamed. This was an iniquity that I had acted upon.

I had stolen from my mother, despite the rationalization I was about to tell the Princes. My iniquity had actualized into a full-blown transgression, and I was deeply sorry. I didn't know how to correct it. Shakespeare's quote, "What's done cannot be undone," did apply. Primal Therapy wouldn't help me with Moses. My voice cracked, as I began to speak.

*Yoseph:* Let me be very clear. I have flagrantly broken the Eighth Commandment. I am the Power of Attorney for my mother, and I have stolen from her estate. She is still living, and I have told her that I have taken some of her monies. However, my confession does not justify what I did. She is in Toronto with dementia or Alzheimer's in a long-term care nursing facility.

I did so with good intentions to help my children and support my application for a Trademark patent for the Shechinah Third Temple, Inc. I took no money for myself. The problem is that I did so without her permission. At the time, approximately four years ago, her mental state was sharp enough for her to make her own decision as to whether she would give me the monies. The one thing my mother did give me in life was to do just that. She was always there to help me when I asked her for monies for the twins' college tuition.

Marcia tried to make me feel better by telling me it was okay, because this was the least my mother could do, having hurt me so much in my life by her negligence. Truthfully, I did reluctantly accept Marcia's words at the time she spoke them because I saw no way out from my shameful deed. My theft has been gnawing at me, and I'm glad I have the chance to confess my sins publicly in this forum.

There was a silence in the room. Michael put his hand on my shoulder. I felt so awful. The pit of my stomach had fallen away. I don't know where it went. I started to cry, and asked forgiveness from my Creator. We were all waiting for Moses to speak. He did so.

*Moses:* Yoseph, you need to find a way out, even if it's imperfect.

For the longest time I didn't reply. Then I spoke from my heart.

*Yoseph:* The Torah talks about *Teshuvah,* or Repentance. I have confessed today, but that is only one-half of *Teshuvah.* The other half is to do a mitzvah or good deed.

When my father died twenty years ago and my brother's lymphoma would, unbeknownst to him, take him two months later, my brother took me to my father's bank. I had no idea that my father had a bank account. There was $30,000 in the account, and my brother split it with me. He even divided the change, down to the penny.

I vow to you in the midst of the Creator, if my mother passes before me, then I will take no money for myself. Like Abraham, this will go against my nature, as I would like to use monies of the estate to promote my Third Temple website and perhaps the new book. My mother had two sons, and I promise to divide all monies equally, between the two families, as I see fit.

I sheepishly looked to Moses. He was reflecting as if he was asking for Divine guidance.

*Moses:* This is an unusual circumstance. Commonly, the intention of the transgression matches exactly to the consequential action of the intention. Yoseph, your original intention when you took the monies was good. You were trying to help your children, and you were trying to help G-d. Nevertheless, your actions were inexcusable, as you broke the Eighth Commandment by stealing from your mother. I believe Abraham found himself in the same pickle. He behaved exactly like you. His intention was good, to be absolutely loyal to G-d. His actions were wrong, because they caused Sarah's death. I condemn you for your sin. However, I applaud you for your goodness toward the Almighty and for your compassion and love for your children. It's not quite a wash, but I'll accept it, even though you were not commanded by G-d, while Abraham was.

Let's move on and reserve judgment, as we agreed to, until we hear more from you, Yoseph.

I hadn't thought about Abraham's test this way. Moses provided a new perspective on Abraham's actions, and surprisingly on mine. I continued.

<u>Ninth Commandment:</u>

*Do not testify as a perjurious witness against your neighbor.*

*Yoseph:* I see these words as commanding us to not spread lies about anyone or slander our friends and others, especially behind their backs or in the courtroom. I adhere to the slander part of this commandment, although I often like to hear about and talk gossip. I need to stop this idle chatter, and I will.

There is no excuse for harming and hurting your fellow when they are not hurting you. Your enemy who is trying to deliberately hurt you is another kettle of fish. It is unnatural to love your enemies, as Jesus proposed. I also place mental and physical abuse under this commandment.

*Tenth Commandment:*

*Do not desire your neighbor's wife.*

*Do not desire your neighbor's house, his field, his male and female slave, his ox, his donkey, or anything else that belongs to your neighbor.*

*Yoseph:* Man's desire, greed, and jealousy are unmatched. I have none of these qualities, except there is still a very residual amount of neurotic inferiority around people who are obviously better than me, like all of you. In the now, my self-esteem and self-confidence have escalated to the point where I can respect and not envy someone else's greatness. I can be content with my own worth. My spirituality and my therapy are allowing me to supersede these negative personality traits and any remaining vestige of inferiority

Eve got into trouble in the Garden of Eden because her desire and lust controlled her, and she lost sight of what she already had. If we have gratitude for who we are and what we have, we shall not wander and stray. Desiring your neighbor's wife can lead to adultery, if you act on your desire with a willing spouse. In the extreme case, desire can lead to rape and even murder.

Unfortunately, many children acquire these traits because they didn't get enough love as children or they had to contend with the favoritism of sibling rivalry. My father favored my brother, and my mother couldn't deliver love. I've always been a big proponent of fairness because of my personal experiences.

*Moses:* You have answered from your heart and the hidden recesses of your mind. Your Primal Therapy has stood you well, permitting you to cast away your defenses. Most people can't do that. You are to be commended.

G-d can see our future by our behavioral patterns. If He sees that we are growing spiritually, He not only considers our past and present, but also our future. When G-d spoke to you with His Voice in your cottage in Poquott and said, "You shall be Mine," He knew the steps you would take to improve your character.

The misfortunes, which we encounter in life, can be blessings in disguise. If we choose the spiritual path, we may, as the Psalm says, reap joy from sadness. Yoseph, you are, in fact, doing this now. Sometimes, it's better to have a yoke in your youth. If your life goes by and you only live in the material world, then when you do face a crisis later on in life, you may sink down into clinical depression. You will lack the spiritual tools to bring yourself out of your misery.

The early part of your life is a testament to your suffering, and you are developing compassion through feeling your sadness in your therapy. If we do not give compassion to others, then how can we expect compassion from the Creator? You are one of the rare fortunate humans who received G-d's compassion at a time when you yourself were not compassionate and not worthy of it. G-d has a Divine plan for you, but I don't honestly know if that is for you to become His Messiah.

Now, I have some short questions to test your knowledge of Torah. The first one is: Why did the Torah begin with the story of Creation?

*Yoseph:* I took some online courses. The answer given by the rabbi was that this introduction would establish the sovereignty of G-d over the earth.

194

*Moses:* Yes, but what's your interpretation?

*Yoseph:* I think to let the world know that only He, G-d, was around with His created angels at the beginning of universal time and space. His intention was to not simply demonstrate His mastery with a long drawn-out time frame of the Universe and Evolution. He wanted to do it almost instantaneously to show the power of His miracles. Most importantly, this was the beginning of Faith, because it's easy to disbelieve if no one else was present to witness the feat. When it came time to witness the Ten Commandments, there were hundreds of thousands of Israelites at Mount Sinai.

*Moses:* Your last statement on Faith was original. Now tell me why Israel was not a nation before the giving of the Ten Commandments.

*Yoseph:* The slavery in Egypt was the prerequisite for the Ten Commandments. As the rabbi metaphorically put it, the Jews needed to break an arm and reset it in a cast. The analogy doesn't answer your question. I think G-d intended to place Israel in the background and the Ten Commandments in the forefront. From my own personal experiences, I see how difficult it is to follow these commandments. These commandments are very much about moral choices, and G-d needed them to represent the final judgment on who would enter the Messianic Age. The Ten Commandments also temporarily arrested the predestined spiritual fall of the Israelites and the First and Second Temples.

*Moses:* Now tell me, why did G-d tell Joshua not to profit from the spoils of war when he conquered the land?

*Yoseph:* G-d was wise enough to see the problems ahead when you do this. We never learned that lesson in Iraq. Oil became our profit motive, and now look at the mess we're in.

*Moses:* Is the Creator a jealous G-d?

*Yoseph:* Only when it comes to the worship of idols. G-d is firm on this; however, the Second Commandment only applies to the Jewish people.

*Moses:* Why did a thousand years of prophecy disappear with idol worship?

*Yoseph:* G-d granted the prayers of the Men of the Great Assembly to eliminate idol worship. If prophecy had remained at that time, there would be no doubt about the future, and free will would be lost.

*Moses:* G-d purposely created a tenuous world in which your enemies can become your friends and your friends your enemies. Can you comment?

*Yoseph:* In Solomon's time, his words, "And the kisses of the enemy are deceptive," rang true in an isolated part of the world with limited enemies. In today's fast-paced, spread-out, geographical world, your friends and enemies can turn on and off like a faucet.

I'm worried about the End of Days, when all of the world may well be Israel's enemy. I think you have to look at who has consistently been Israel's enemy and consider them as a possible initiator of an apocalyptic war at the End of Days. I don't think you can look at your friends, because they may get swept up in the heat of the battle. It is more likely that friends will switch to fight on the side of their enemies, rather than enemies switching to fight alongside your allies. The prophecies are pretty clear on this.

*Moses:* And who are the apocalyptic enemies in your opinion?

*Yoseph:* The descendants of Isaac's stepbrother, Ishmael. The hearts of the nation of Islam are false, when they murder and maim the innocent. Their desire is to wipe Israel off the map. You can't negotiate with murderers, for this just emboldens them. Like the ancient Canaanites, the Islamic fundamentalists are not G-d's works. They are the evil without a stamp of the Divine. G-d placed evil alongside good so that evil can be defeated. At the End of Days, we shall see the destruction of all evil by G-d.

*Moses:* You don't have to elaborate. I understand that you will have a surprise interviewer later on. Oops, I guess I let the cat out of the bag, to use a modern expression. Are the Israelis apartheid?

*Yoseph:* The Land was given by G-d to Abraham, Isaac, and Jacob, and G-d's Torah passed through Isaac but not Ishmael. I think that modern Israel would like to live in peace; however, terrorist and even peaceful factions within the Muslim world won't let them. They have no choice but to protect themselves. When Joshua crossed the Jordan, he gave the Canaanite nations three distinct choices:

Live in peace.

Leave.

Die in war.

Joshua conquered and settled the Land, but he didn't kill all of the Canaanites. This merciful decision had its pluses and minuses. Individual Canaanites played an integral part of Jewish history. King David purchased the land for the First Temple from Aravnah the Jebusite. However, the descendants of the

Canaanites, for example, the Philistines, lived to fight another day. The Palestinians are descendants of the Philistines. They were converted to monotheism by the prophet Muhammad. The three friends in Nebuchadnezzar's Babylonian exile, Chananyah, Azaryah, and Mishael were descendants from Jews who made the Golden Calf.

*Moses:* Can man nullify any of the Ten Commandments? A rhetorical question that still needs an answer.

*Yoseph:* Apparently so, since man has just done that. However, man has no jurisdiction to eradicate what G-d has bound him to do. He can choose to follow or not follow the Ten Commandments, but he must realize that he is accountable at Judgment Day, and he, therefore, does so at his own peril.

*Moses:* Do you have sufficient *anavah*, humility, for the task at hand?

Ysoeph: I'm getting there.

*Moses:* What does humility mean to you?

*Yoseph:* I quote with slight word modification from *Deuteronomy 8:17-18*: *"It is not your (my) own strength and personal power that has brought you (me) all this prosperity (to be the person who I am), for you (I) must remember that it is G-d, your L-rd, who gives you (me) the power to become prosperous (to have the opportunity to succeed in my endeavors)."*

In the final analysis, all that I have been given, I owe to G-d. There is an inner security of belief and total faith in G-d. I can be much calmer about my doubts and uncertainties of the future.

*Moses:* Do you think that someone else might do a better job than you, either with your G-d-given talents or with their own?

*Yoseph:* Yes. If I did not feel this way, I would not be humble.

*Moses:* Can you recommend someone other than yourself.

*Yoseph:* Yes, but it's too dangerous to provide you with a name.

*Moses:* Reading my mind. I understand. Why hasn't the Messianic Age come before its appointed time? The prophets tell us that the Messianic Age can come at any time if we are ready.

*Yoseph:* I don't know whether I shall be the Messiah. I think we shall not be ready until G-d chooses the time for His Messiah to stand with Him.

G-d waited two thousand years, after the Creation, for Abraham. Noah was a righteous man, and was chosen to build the Ark. However, Abraham had the special qualities of kindness and persuasiveness that G-d was looking for in a man in order to spread His monotheism. I won't flatter you, Moses, but the same is true for you, and you Jacob, and you King David.

*Moses:* Oh! I see now. "Out of many comes *only* one." Abraham back in biblical times, and the Messiah soon.

We all laughed. Moses had stolen my quote.

*Moses:* Are you claiming that G-d spoke to me the way He spoke to you?

*Yoseph:* A parting shot? No, but He did speak to me.

*Moses:* Good. You were honest and didn't flatter me. I detest insincerity.

I must say I'm warming up to you. You have a way about you, a winning personality. Your wife tells me that you like to smile. If you are chosen as the Messiah, rest assured, all of us will be smiling together. Joy and laughter will be the hallmark of the Messianic Age. As Isaiah vocalizes, children will play in the streets, and so will the adults.

I know just what you are thinking. When did I speak to your wife? Both of us are telepathic. Of course, you know that about Marcia.

*Yoseph:* (I relaxed and smiled.) Thank you Moses. I am truly honored by your comments and your friendship.

All of the Princes were clapping and hugging each other, as if they were celebrating a grand wedding.

*King David:* On this joyous note, we will end our half-day session, and we will meet again tomorrow.

*Michael:* Another day. You did well again, Yoseph. I'll see you tomorrow.

Marcia was waiting for me at the South Gate of the Outer Courtyard. She was wearing a gold sundress that sparkled in the sunlight. Her dress went spinning as I picked her up and swirled her round and round until we both were dizzy and fell to the ground.

There was a Purim concert in the Temple Mount. The lawn was filled with thousands of angels who were dancing with their wings flying in the breeze. The Levites were performing their tunes about the evil Haman, the incredibly beautiful Queen Esther, the wise Mordechai, and the Jewish people to the music of the Wizard of Oz. The Levite singers were singing, "Follow the road to the East," to Jerusalem, instead of, "Follow the yellow brick road." One of the angels was acting out the role of Haman. He was dressed in black tights and had pitch-black horns, a red cape, and a witch's broomstick, so I couldn't tell whether the evil Haman was supposed to represent the wicked witch of the west or the fallen angel, Satan. Whoever he was, he needed to see a dentist, as his teeth were all stained yellow, and he emitted a foul-smelling odor from his mouth.

The Festival of Purim began some 2,500 years ago, and it was the last time that G-d performed His miracles to save the Jews. When I looked up on the dais, I thought I recognized the rabbis and cantors from our congregation in Boca Raton. They were performing various roles from the Wizard of Oz, adapted to Purim. I swear I even saw myself on stage, dressed as a munchkin, as I was a member of the synagogue's choir. I could carry a tune, but as I told the cantor repeatedly, "I don't have a voice."

The air smelled of lilacs, and oddly enough, I imagined I saw poppies. After all, we were in heaven—*Over The Rainbow.* Marcia and I lied down and fell asleep on the unusual softness of the ground. Our bodies seemed to contour to this natural mattress. When we awakened, we found ourselves lying in our comfy bed at home. I wondered if we had been dreaming. Maybe this whole heavenly adventure was a dream.

# 19

# JACOB

*M*ARCIA MADE A BREAKFAST* of eggs easy over, multigrain toast with fresh blueberry preserve, and decaffeinated coffee. There was no bacon in heaven. The eggs were hatched from free-range chickens, and I couldn't help wonder if the principles in charge of heaven realized the difference between free-range eggs and eggs laid from grain-fed chickens cooped up in spaceless cages with their beaks snapped off. I laughed to myself when I imagined this question being asked today at the Messiah Interviews.

Elementary, my dear Jacob or Abraham. Organic eggs have a ratio between one-to-one or two-to-one of the essential fatty acids, the omega 6 to omega 3 ratio. The ratio in grain-fed eggs rises as high as eighteen-to-one. Not necessarily good for the heart. Only the organic eggs have the right parent ratio for incorporation of the essential fatty acids into our cell membranes. A yet unproven suggestion has been proposed. The higher non-organic omega 6 to omega 3 ratios could be problematic for diffusion of oxygen into our cells, with consequential development of cancer.

I took a different path back to the Temple and found myself wandering through a garden of roses. Whoever was the keeper of the garden was a natural horticulturist. Every color of the rainbow, in addition to black and white, was represented. The gardener obviously knew something about plant genetics, as there were multiple hybrid species. I felt like a honeybee sniffing its way from rose to rose. The roses gave me an incredible high.

I arrived at the Temple, and all of the Princes were seated and waiting for me. I checked my watch. I was punctual. Abraham and Jacob were huddled together. I presumed they were making a determination on who would be the next interviewer. Jacob convinced his grandfather that it would be best if Abraham went last. The relevance of their decision was beyond me.

*Jacob:* (Chuckling) Good morning, Yoseph. I appreciate your thoughts about chickens and eggs. I, too, dabbled in science. It was when I was with Laban. Do you remember the speckled cows?

*Yoseph:* Yes I do. I remember how Laban tried to cheat you and how you outsmarted him.

*Jacob:* Can you offer any take-home lesson from my twenty years with Laban? Recall that the first seven years were for Leah, the next seven for Rachel, and then an additional six years and two more marriages to build equity independence from Laban.

*Yoseph:* Yes, I can provide some illumination on your journey. G-d desires us to work hard so that we can appreciate our efforts and be grateful for the worldly pleasures, which we can gain through human physical or mental labor. He also puts obstacles in our paths to test our resolve to complete our goals or our mission. Jacob, after being tricked into a marriage with Leah, you needed to work a second set of seven years to win your true love, Rachel. You have given so much of yourself by dedicating a lifetime to father the Twelve Tribes, which became the Jewish nation.

I have spent the past ten years of spiritual learning in order to be able to only now write the book on the Messiah Interviews. My goal is to follow in Abraham's footsteps and bring earthly awareness and recognition of G-d's Holiness. Remarkably, G-d seems to be fading from Judaism. If I become the Messiah and build G-d's Third Temple, then my life, like yours, will be dedicated to a Higher purpose.

*Jacob:* Well spoken. Do you pray, Yoseph?

*Yoseph:* Yes, but not often enough.

*Jacob:* What do you think is the significance of prayer?

*Yoseph:* It's an opportunity to take a quiet, powerful moment away from the fray of the noise of life and communicate your requests to the Creator with sincerity in your heart. G-d may answer your prayers, even if truth and honesty are missing. He can still grant your requests if He has looked into your heart and seen future potential of sincerity within you. G-d knows whether it's only a matter of time until you will grow and mature into your righteousness. G-d has always responded to my prayers. At the beginning of my journey, I was undeserving. In the present, I feel I still am unworthy, and that's after ten years of climbing the spiritual ladder.

In my humble opinion, pious individuals do not automatically warrant their prayers to be fulfilled. As the Book of Isaiah, *Isaiah 29:13*, clearly states, *"These people draw near with their mouth. They honor Me with their lips, but their heart is far from Me."*

In general, if you don't pray, and to boot, you doubt
G-d, it seems unreasonable for you to expect His assistance.
Yet, G-d's Ways are not our ways. If He does provide undisclosed help to a non-believer, He must have a very good
reason for doing so.

*Jacob:* Do you consider yourself a righteous person?

*Yoseph:* No one should consider himself righteous. That's
up to G-d to determine, and we'll only know who is righteous
at the End of Days. If I am deemed righteous, I will never
take my righteousness for granted. I will not depend upon
my past deeds.

You, Isaac, and Abraham are our Patriarchs. I am honored
to be speaking with you. On your return from your sojourn with
Laban, G-d told you that he would protect you from your brother
Esau. You never took G-d for granted. You prayed, gave gifts to
Esau, and prepared for battle. In the end, you knew that all your
planning for your meeting with Esau would be secondary to G-d
determining your fate and destiny with your brother.

*Jacob:* Yes, what you say is true. How does charitable giving
relate to righteousness? The Hebrew Bible states that charity
can save you from death.

*Yoseph:* I'll quote from Solomon's Book of Proverbs, *"One
who closes his ears to the pauper, he too will call out to G-d
and not be answered."* Charity, or *tzedakah* in Hebrew, is an
essential component of righteousness. It was you, Jacob, who
allocated one-tenth of his income to G-d.

Giving charity does not absolve you from feeling superior. Job typically acted arrogantly. There is an expression for
Job's generosity. He can be described as a *tzaddik*, a righteous
person, in *pelz*. When it's cold outside, Job can be found

wearing his *pelz*, his warm fur coat. He struts around like a peacock while all around him our starving sparrows.

*Jacob:* A good analogy. Do you know why the Torah is likened to a fig tree?

*Yoseph:* A fig is delicious through and through. So is the Torah. Solomon says that if you guard the fig tree, you will reap it fruits. If you follow the ways of the Torah in your heart and soul, you will be rewarded by G-d.

Jacob. What does following the Torah mean to you?

*Yoseph:* Follow the Ten Commandments, and express love, mercy, and compassion from your soul. Perform good deeds for G-d and fellow man, including acts of charity. Pray to G-d, because He is silently asking us to do so. Be a *mensch*, and not hurt anyone. Stand up for justice and speak out against wrong in our world, even if it's not popular or it is dangerous to do so. Love, praise, and honor G-d. Be grateful and appreciative. Always be aware of those who went before us. Complete our mission to help the Jewish people.

*Jacob:* That's quite a list. What does fear and awe of G-d mean to you?

*Yoseph:* I interpret these words to have two separate meanings.

Awe signifies the appreciation of G-d's wondrous universe. Fear doesn't mean that I'm afraid of G-d. Fear implies that I'm afraid to lose G-d's love, so I'm very careful in my actions. I believe that fear of G-d was created by G-d. In the non-believer, fear resides at a subliminal level, surfacing when major tragedy strikes.

*Jacob:* Do you crave wealth? Are you one of those people who never has enough?

*Yoseph:* I have sufficient money. I am, however, frustrated by my inability to initiate the necessary momentum to build an awareness of the importance of the future Third Temple. Some of my kids also need help. I do play the lottery, when the jackpot gets above eighteen million. I think you actually wind up leading an impoverished life when you have enough wealth but still continue to chase money.

*Jacob:* What do the characters in the Torah teach us? Are they just historical figures?

*Yoseph:* The lives of the Patriarchs depict scenes that are forerunners of events in man's future. The sages and prophets show us archetypical personalities that bear semblances of reality to our own character traits. The Torah's descriptions provide us with the full spectrum of human emotions.

*Jacob:* Why do you think my father went blind? Was it old age? He did live to 180 years.

*Yoseph:* Age is one possibility. It is also conceivable that G-d's Hand was indirectly involved. That is, Divine Providence was operating. You may not have accomplished what you did in your life if your father was not blind. That's how you and your mother, Rebecca, fooled Isaac into thinking you were Esau. The truth is that Isaac knew that you were Jacob, but he gave you Esau's blessing anyway.

Isaac also knew that G-d had blinded him, because he would have favored your brother Esau with his blessing. G-d desired you, Jacob, to fulfill His Covenant with Israel, just as He wanted David to be king after Saul's reign. As a wise sage remarked, "To bring a new generation into the world, is an ambition worthy of any mother. Jacob's four wives were giving birth to a nation."

*Jacob:* Earlier, we talked about righteousness. Now tell me, what is spirituality?

*Yoseph:* Rabbi Pliskin says that when you have a spiritual outlook, you realize that things turn out exactly as they should. You try to do what G-d would expect of you so that you can expect of Him—that is, expect His aid in your endeavors. This doesn't mean you are a fatalist.

Being spiritual means that you look heavenward and become G-d-centered, instead of self-centered. Spirituality is not something you are born with. You need to acquire it gradually through a brute force learning curve. Once you do obtain it, you view everything in life as a gift from the Creator. You place yourself in G-d's Hands, after you have done your best on your own. G-d determines the ultimate outcome, as you, Jacob, well understood with your brother Esau. There are no coincidences.

When you are spiritual, you can make others feel good. All you have to do is be yourself, and you touch their hearts. A spiritual person empowers. A leader without spirituality only inspires.

*Jacob:* Your ego is not concealing your Divine Soul. You have proven in all our interviews that you are not only wise but also discerning, like your namesake, my son Yoseph. Yes, you have acquired knowledge from others. You also possess an original and creative mind, and you are not dependent on others' thinking or influence. That's the definition of discernment.

A Messiah has to be above the influence of the thinking of men, even his most trusted advisors. You seem to have a special gift. Your Primal Therapy has made you a deep, feeling human being while your spirituality has made you a deep thinker. You may not be as intelligent as many of the human race, but you do have wisdom. If you become the Messiah, G-d will provide for the rest of what you will need.

I'm going to ask that King David call a thirty-minute coffee break before I resume.

*King David:* I think that's a good idea. We can offer sweets and drinks in the Outer Courtyard.

I walked out with Michael. King David came over and started to tell me about his life and what mine would be like if I were successful. I wondered how much I was willing to give up? King David then spoke.

*King David:* Your life is no longer your own.

All the Princes gathered around and began to chat. I felt no animosity, only warmth and friendship. I wished Marcia were here. She would have been so proud. The sound of a bell signaled the return to the Sanctuary.

*Jacob:* You remind me so much of my son Yoseph. He could have been the Messiah, if he lived in a different age. He had great wisdom and depth of character. In Jewish history, we speak only about three Patriarchs. There is no doubt, in my mind, that he was a fourth.

*Yoseph:* Thank you for the compliment. I don't deserve such praise. I haven't earned it. I haven't done anything in my life that remotely compares to your son. He was a great *tzaddik.*

*Jacob:* How modest of you, Yoseph. Now, we need to talk about a problem that you alluded to previously in the interview process. You need to discuss the Ten Lost Tribes. In Messianic times, all Jews are destined to return to the Land of Israel, which will be divided equally among the Twelve Tribes.

*Yoseph:* I can attempt this. However, I'll need to back up my answer with quotes cited from the United Israel movement in the United States. I have read the material on their website, and it makes sense to me.

*Jacob:* Then do so.

*Yoseph:* When the Ten Northern Tribes split from the Southern Tribes of Judah and Benjamin, they corrupted the Ten Commandments, particularly by removing G-d from their temples and replacing Him with idols. For their wickedness, they were punished by G-d through death and exile by King Sancherib and the Assyrians, approximately 130 years prior to the Babylonian exile of the two Southern Tribes.

Only the Southern Tribes continued to be known as G-d's people. The Northern Tribes lost both G-d and their identity as Jews. They became non–Jews or gentiles. *Jeremiah 31* talks to Ephraim, synonymous with the Ten Lost Tribes, streaming in from the north country and from the furthest parts of the earth to join Judah, the two Southern Tribes, and the Levites and *kohanim*. The descendants of the Lost Northern Tribes will return to Israel from places in northwestern Europe like Germany and Scandinavia, from Great Britain, and from the British Empire, including the United States. These descendants are Protestants, especially Protestant Evangelicals, who have a biblical and political affinity for Israel as well as a common history of persecution.

According to the definition of *lost*, the Lost Tribes do not know their identity as descendants. If they did, they would not be *lost*. The process of marital assimilation into gentile society occurred hundreds or even thousands of years ago. It is Rachel, weeping for her son Joseph, who touches G-d's Heart.

G-d promises Rachel that one day the Lost Tribes, including Joseph's Tribe—represented by the tribes of his two sons, the Tribes of Ephraim and Manasseh—will return to Israel to reconstitute the Twelve Tribes.

It is written by the prophets, *"And the people of Judah and the people of Israel, the Ten Northern Tribes, shall be gathered together, and they shall appoint for themselves one head (King Messiah)."* It will be G-d and His servant, the Messiah, who will gather in the House of Israel, the Northern Tribes, and the House of Judah, the Southern Tribes. Both Houses are referred to as the two sticks. G-d will cleanse the Twelve Tribes of all their iniquities, so they will have a new heart and a new spirit. G-d will do this by sprinkling Holy water from the future Third Temple on each of those who is returned to Israel.

The Hebrew prophets are very clear. The End of Days will bring on the age of G-d. Christianity interprets G-d, Himself, as being Jesus the Messiah, but the Hebrew Scriptures indicate that the unification will be brought about by G-d, primarily. The role of the Messiah seems to be minor, until the coming together of the two sticks, the Twelve Tribes. At this future time, there will be a transformation and purification of the entire world.

It is difficult to estimate quantitatively what percentage of the Jews who are living as non-Jews will return for the Redemption and the Messianic Age. The Bible seems to suggest that G-d will pluck them out one by one, as a shepherd gathers the sheep of his flock. Yet, in *Isaiah 10:22*, we find, *"For though your people, Israel, (the Ten Northern Tribes) bear the sand of the sea, (only) a remnant of them shall return."* It may be that of the ones that G-d plucks, from every nook and cranny, only a select number will be brought back to unite with the two Southern Tribes. The basis for the return would be judgment on their morality, and even if selected, these individuals will have to be purified of their sins. The same is true for we Jews living as Jews in our modern world.

Today's Jews are represented by the Tribes of Judah, Benjamin, the Levites, the *kohanim*, and any of the Northern Tribes who returned with the Jews from the Babylonian exile. Today, modern Jews don't know which tribe—Judah, Benjamin, or one of the Northern Tribes—we belong to.

It's very confusing, because we have descendants of the Northern Tribes living as Jews, who are not lost, and millions or tens of millions living as Protestants, who don't know their ancestors were Jews.

To complicate the story further, there are many individuals, living around the world, who claim ancestry to the Lost Tribes. Some have legitimate claims while others may not, and it's a mess. I'm not talking about African Jews that can show direct genetic lineage to the High Priests, the *kohanim*. The State of Israel is being inundated with millions of Africans and Asians claiming to be of Jewish descent. Large numbers have already moved to Israel and have been integrated into the society of the Jewish State.

*Jacob:* Thank you for explaining. I now see the magnitude of the problem. I know that in biblical times, the borders of present-day Israel will be expanded to the north into Lebanon and Syria and to the east into Jordan, but how will we accommodate all these people. Moreover, it sounds like all Jews will be ingathered to Israel, including those from America. What are your comments?

*Yoseph:* I just don't know, Jacob. Perhaps, we shall really have to enter the Messianic Age with a "B" grade. This still makes the most sense to me, as then the population numbers may be manageable.

*Jacob:* We Princes have food for thought, speaking of which, let's break early for lunch.

*King David:* We shall meet back here at 2 p.m. Tonight, we shall have a banquet, Yoseph, and we would like you and Marcia to attend. I've already sent Elijah the prophet to inform her.

*Yoseph:* Thank you all.

The lunch break was about two and a half hours, so I decided to return home and take a dip in the pool. Marcia joined me, and I told her all about Jacob's interview. The water in the pool sparkled like diamonds as ducks swam by in the lake. There was a great blue heron that was looking through our screened-in patio and smiling at us. The orchid tree was full of purple orchids, and our one rose bush was blooming with coral roses. Croton shrubs with tri-colored green, yellow, and orange leaves, red Ti plants, and coral and pink Hibiscus flowers blended in with the purple Bougainvillea bushes. The day was magnificent. I hugged Marcia and then made my way over familiar grounds of the Temple Mount.

# 20

# ABRAHAM

*A*BRAHAM, G-D'S CHOICE to kick off monotheism. Why only three religions? Surely, it was unconscionable that the whole world didn't believe in G-d's world. Were Buddhism, Hinduism, Taoism, etc., products of Evolution, Creation, or both? Noah's Ark and the Flood could only have taken place in an isolated but bustling part of the world. Evolution human existed long before and had survived and evolved independent of Creation human. Did Creation humans procreate with Evolution humans? Might the latter possibility explain why the human race looks so different among its population? DNA genetics cannot answer these questions, because G-d scrambled Creation and Evolution genetics when He created Adam with a DNA inherited without the normal rite of passage of a sperm and an egg. Miraculous? Yes.

*Abraham:* I know what you're thinking, Yoseph. That's why G-d's intelligence is infinite and ours is so limited. Science can be duplicated, but not miracles. It is meant to be that we don't understand G-d's Essence now. We shall get to know G-d in the Messianic Age.

We humans are an odd bunch. We not only criticize our contemporaries for antiquated beliefs. We also disbelieve the Creator, and some go so far as to ridicule Him for His ancient Torah stories. Sometimes, I feel like a relic that has been polished and put up for auction.

I am the Father of three religions: Judaism, Christianity, and Islam. I am very saddened at the hostility among us. We have moved so far to the right that we not only cannot tolerate one another, we hate each other. Look at past history, and look at your modern world. Pathetic!

My grandson, Jacob, started out with a family of seventy when he went down to Goshen in the land of Egypt at the invitation of my great grandson, Joseph, then Viceroy to the Pharaoh. By the time the Israelites reached Mount Sinai, their numbers had swelled to the hundreds of thousands. Some say about two million, although the math may not hold up over a 210-year period of slavery.

I have seen much in my lifetime. I bore two sons, Isaac and Ishmael, both of whom went on to be the forerunners of two monotheistic religions: Judaism and Islam. Through my seed came Jesus, a mighty orator of such charisma and sensitivity that a whole new religion, Christianity, evolved from just him, one singular human being.

My question to you, Yoseph, is not concerning the conflicts of humankind in today's world; G-d has predestined dishar-mony, so we may know harmony in the future. I want you to tell me the historical role of each of our three monotheistic reli-gions toward our progress and also our detriment in arriving at the future Messianic world.

*Yoseph:* A whopper of a request. How do I answer such a complicated question?

Unfortunately, I am not a Hebrew prophet. I have no crystal ball to forecast the future. Nor am I a historian who can speak in volumes about the past. I only have whatever wisdom and insight that G-d has graciously granted me. I think we all know that, according to the Torah, there are two scenarios to the Messianic Age. Both the New Testament and the Qur'an talk about only one outcome: an apocalyptic ending to earth. The second Torah option, which seems more and more unlikely to me, is that we march together in splendor into the Messianic Age.

We humans have failed to charter our course. As Shakespeare aptly said, *"The fault dear Brutus is not in our stars, but in ourselves."* I'm afraid the outcome for the world looks bleak.

The Messianic Age will come at G-d's appointed time, if this world ends in violence. Or, it will come in human time, if our world comes together in harmony. You, Abraham, pleaded with G-d to save Sodom, a biblical city of moral depravity. G-d first told you that He would honor your request if you could find fifty men of admirable qualities. You could not. You argued that G-d should save the city if there were only ten men of goodness. There were not. The city burned with all its inhabitants, except for the families of your nephew, Lot, and yourself.

G-d's Divine Providence is unclear and has twists and turns. It would be Lot's descendants who would give birth to Ruth the Moabite princess. Ruth would follow her Jewish

mother-in-law, Naomi. In that famous scene on the fields of
Moab, Naomi tries to discourage Ruth from accompanying her
to Israel. Ruth speaks those magnificent inspiring words.

*"For where you go, I will go.*
*Your people are my people.*
*Your G-d is my G-d.*
*Wherever you die, I will die."*

Ruth marries Boaz of the Tribe of Judah, and they become
the great grandparents of King David and the ancestors of the
Messiah.

Assuming that I am part of Ruth's genetic lineage and I
become the Messiah, I will declare an international monthly
holiday, the time of the New Moon, for G-d. History has
taught us that it is all too easy to forget the Creator, especially
in good times. We need G-d to find life, but too much focus
on G-d may prevent us from living and enjoying life. G-d
doesn't demand our complete attention. However, like us, He
needs recognition.

A holiday for G-d, at which time we bring our Divine
Souls together, seems impossible in modern times. Everyone
is preaching the gospel to prove that his or her religion is the
true religion of G-d. Each of the three monotheistic religions
proclaims absolute truth and Divine authority, and is quick to
criticize the other two for their Faith. Strikingly, there is bitterness, disunity, and intolerance among the subgroups within
each faction. Christians, Muslims, and Jews have a lot riding
on G-d's Judgment Day at the End of Days. Who will be the
chosen religion among human beings? My answer is that it

will be those from all religions, who, based upon their moral merits, will be admitted by G-d into the Messianic Age.

*Abraham:* Yoseph, I find this whole discussion fascinating, but you are not answering my question.

*Yoseph:* I apologize for wandering off topic. Marcja always tells me that I should have been a politician, because I never answer her questions directly.

(The Princes had a light moment of laughter.)

*Yoseph:* All I can go by is what's written about the past and the future. As I said, I can't predict the future. Let's start with the New Testament.

The Gospels of Matthew, Mark, and Luke speak to Jesus' description of the End of Days. There will be mistrust, deception, starvation, hatred, and violent wars of incomparable destruction. Jesus will return as the Messiah to the Mount of Olives and Jerusalem and usher in a 1,000-year period of peace and prosperity. In the Christian faith, Israel's very survival is dependent upon the return of Jesus from heaven.

According to the Book of Revelations, not all the population will die, and those who survive the chaos will be transformed. There will be resurrection of the dead, and with the rapture of the second coming of Jesus, a seven-year period will befall mankind, a time of tribulation, when the world will feel the wrath of G-d. During the death of so many, a false peace will be guaranteed by a rising political star, who is referred to as the Beast or Antichrist. The Temple will be rebuilt in Jerusalem. Then the evil of the Antichrist will be exposed, as he attempts to gain control of the planet. The mark of the Beast will be 666. Half the population of the earth will be destroyed, Jerusalem will be in shambles, and the Jews will flee. Jesus will appear, confront, and defeat this descendant of Satan, and will become G-d's Light in the new world.

*Abraham:* And the Hebrew Bible's description?

*Yoseph:* I'm more familiar with the Jewish writings; I probably am not accurate on the Christian description. The Hebrew Bible talks about the Wars of Gog and Magog. No one knows for sure who or what Gog and Magog refer to, although some have speculated, myself included, as to the significance of these names. Thirteen prophets, as well as King David in Psalms and the righteous Daniel, vividly foretell of the final Redemption—Isaiah, Jeremiah, Ezekiel, Hoshea, Joel, Amos, Obadiah, Micah, Habbakuk, Zephania, Chaggai, Zecharia, and Malachi. The wars will be fought as a series of cataclysmic battles, prior to the Redemption. It is not clear what the role of the *Pafkod Rifked*, the Redeemer, is in the Wars of Gog and Magog. The Messiah may not be directly involved in the actual battles, although he could play an indirect role.

The armies of Gog and Magog, the descendants of the seventy nations of Noah's three sons, will come toward Jerusalem three times and will reach the city on the third try. A siege will take place, but ultimately G-d will step in to slay the oppressors. Only one-third of the population will survive. Peace will be restored between the Northern and Southern Tribes. The prophet, Micah, will oversee the repentance of the surviving Jews. Redemption means to save from sin or its consequences. The survivors will need to be purified.

As foretold by the prophet Zecharia, a great earthquake will mark the *Shechinah's* return in the days of the *Moshiach*, the Messiah. The meaning of the prophet, Jonah, killing the Leviathan sea monster at the End of Days for a banquet of the righteous is not clear, at least to me. Further, it will be another prophet, Elijah, who will enter the presently blocked Golden Gate in the walled city of Jerusalem to usher in the new era. Elijah is thought to precede the Messiah by three days. This scenario is also not clear to me. What is definitive is that the Torah will once again emanate from Mount Zion, and the Word of G-d shall emerge from Jerusalem. The Ark of the Covenant and the Ten Commandments will return in the days of the Messiah. In addition to the seven Princes, there also will be seven Men of High Standing to assist the Messiah: Jesse, the father of David; Saul, from the Tribe of Benjamin and the first king of Israel; Samuel, G-d's loyal prophet; the good Judean king, Hezekia; and three more Hebrew prophets, Zephania, Amos, and Elijah.

According to scriptures, the Messiah may come at any time. *Psalms 95:7* says, *"I will come today if you but heed the voice."* Or, *Isaiah 60:22*: *"Redemption will occur at its appointed time. I will hasten it."* In the Book of Jeremiah, we read, *"Behold the days come, says the L-rd of Hosts, that I shall raise unto David's righteous a Branch, who shall reign as king and deal wisely, and shall execute justice and righteousness in the land."* The Branch, *Zemach*, refers to the Messiah.

When G-d appears at the End of Days, a radiance as brilliant as the Supernal Light that shone during the Seven Days of Creation will be unleashed in all its glory. This Light will represent neither day nor night, and will be the Light emitted from the Holy of Holies of the Third Temple in heaven, or from the Third Temple on earth, if the Temple is built prior to the Redemption. The *Shofar* of the Messiah shall blow at the Redemption to herald in universal peace. Future miracles will be *"incredible to Me,"* says the L-rd of Hosts.

*Abraham:* And the role of Islam?

*Yoseph:* I know that the prophet, Muhammad, was a descendant of your son, Ishmael, whom you loved dearly. I shudder to say, that the Muslim nations will lead the charge against Israel at the End of Days. That's what I think Daniel saw in his visions and dreams of the final Redemption.

*Abraham:* Who is the antichrist, or Daniel's little horn, who devours the earth at the End of Days?

*Yoseph:* I don't know.

*Abraham:* Neither do I. How do you appease Christians if you are selected as Messiah, rather than Jesus?

*Yoseph:* This is obviously a very sensitive issue. If Jesus is chosen, then I would support him, and G-d's decision. However, I don't know how Christians will feel if a Jew, other than Jesus, is the Messiah.

*Abraham:* Have you ever heard the term, *Gilgul HaNeshamos*?

*Yoseph:* Yes. It means that you have the soul of someone who lived in past times and you are accountable for the unresolved sins of that person.

*Abraham:* Do you feel you have the soul of a person from the past?

*Yoseph:* Yes. I have suffered in my life and confessed my sins publicly. Judah confessed his sins publicly, and so did King David. Although Judah did not suffer, King David was tormented for much of his life. I was, too.

*Abraham:* Are you saying that the same soul can be incarnated into different bodies, if G-d so chooses?

*Yoseph:* That's exactly what I'm saying.

*Abraham:* How is this related to the Messiah?

*Yoseph:* I believe that an additional reason we have not entered the Messianic Age is because more time is needed for the refinement of the soul of the Messiah. The soul gains or loses desirable attributes when it occupies different bodies. My soul's refinement, if true, may be exactly right for a perfect or imperfect Messiah's body-and-soul combination.

*Abraham:* A most interesting hypothesis. You might even have Jesus' soul, if he is on the genetic pathway of King David. I have nothing more to add.

*King David:* Thank you all for your stimulating participation. Don't forget about tonight's banquet, Yoseph. Your interviews are not finished. We Princes, however, take our leave after the banquet.

*Yoseph:* It has been an honor and a pleasure. I won't say goodbye until tonight.

*Michael:* Yoseph, I'll accompany you home on foot and then fly back. The late afternoon is a beautiful tranquil time to walk in the garden of the Temple Mount.

# 21

# THE BANQUET

*M*ARCIA LOOKED STUNNING in her black dress and cultured, pink pearls. I decided to dress appropriately and wore my black suit. I chose a white cuffed, long-sleeved shirt, a modest black and red striped tie, and my twenty-five years of service Stony Brook tie tack. My choice of white was my feeble attempt to match the purity of the evening ahead.

The banquet was held in the Inner Courtyard of the Temple under the stars and the moonlit sky. Scientists say that we use only 1 percent of our brain's capacity. In the interviews, I felt that I had connected to the reality of the remaining 99 percent. Tonight was to be a few hours to turn my brain off. As we entered the East Gate to the Temple, the Levite musicians and choir had already begun to play and sing tunes from King David's Psalms.

Two circular tables, each seating ten with white linen table cloths, matching cloth napkins, and place cards, were set up with sterling silver cutlery and bone china plates. Each of the two tables had complimentary, antique silver vases, filled with two dozen yellow roses, freshly cut from the rose garden of the Temple Mount. Our waiters for the evening were the Levite priests, all dressed in white robes. Everyone looked spectacular in biblical evening clothes, and the outside air had the most enticing perfume odor, which engulfed our senses. The heavenly setting was picture perfect, and I could feel the excitement and sparkles in my body.

My table consisted of the seven Princes, Marcia, me, and a blank setting that I was told was reserved for G-d. The other table had Gabriel, Michael, Tzaddok, and the noble seven Men of High Standing—Jesse, Saul, Samuel, Hezekia, Zephania, Amos, and Elijah. Tzaddok made the blessings over the wine and *challah*, and I was asked to make a toast. I was speechless, so Michael came to my rescue.

Michael's toast was a very simple prayer.

*Michael:* We are gathered here on this auspicious occasion
to honor and praise G-d. May He bless us all, so that we may
continue to serve Him.

All said Amen.

Then unexpectedly, Jacob stood up and made a special blessing for Marcia, me, and our family. I was deeply touched. I had read that when the righteous confer a blessing, it is a privilege granted by G-d, who provides the metaphysical force to make the blessing efficacious. I surmised that, like blessings, prayers from people of faith for a sick person they don't even know work because G-d, too, receives the prayers and passes them on to the ill recipient.

There was a tapping of the silver goblets to drink up, and for me to kiss Marcia. The Levites kept filling our cups, and my head was spinning in joyful bliss. Before I had a chance to refuse, Moses pulled me up onto the marble floor, and all of us joined hands in one large circle and danced the traditional Jewish *Hora*. My legs never kicked so high, and we were all roaring with laughter. At one point, Tzaddok dragged me to the center of the circle to do a Chassidic dance with him. I was embarrassed by all the attention.

Our main course was one of my favorites: brisket with potato pancake, and kasha and varnishkes. Tears came to my eyes, as I thought about my paternal grandmother, Lily, who made kasha for me almost every day when I was a child growing up. I never tired of the food, or her Yiddish, which I never understood. I thought of all my grandparents, my brother Norm, my father, and Yinnon, and I started to bawl. I was hoping I would meet the deceased once again during the Resurrection. I wished I had life to do all over again so I could tell them how much I love them and miss them.

More wine and several hours later, and it was almost time to go to sleep. Then the tinkling of the goblets. This time, I was asked to say a few words. There were tears in my eyes as I looked straight into the eyes of each and every person, and at the two angels.

I got up a little wobbly, with Marcia clutching my hand.

*Yoseph:* Usually a *mitzvah* is a two-way street. The wealthy person does a kind deed for the pauper. The pauper, in turn, does a kindness for the wealthy person by providing him with the opportunity to do the *mitzvah*. Both persons are required in order to fulfill the *mitzvah*. However, the *mitzvah* of the Messiah Interviews in heaven doesn't belong to me. It belongs only to you and the Creator. You have melted my soul, and I am so grateful just to be with you. I shall never forget the opportunity to soar with angels. You are all angels, and I shall miss you terribly. You always shall be with me.

I sat down, and all stood up to give me an ovation and wish me luck. I hugged each one of them, and Marcia and I made our way out of the Temple grounds. We could still hear the Levites playing. In honor of us, we heard Kenny Rogers' tune, *Through the Years*, as we walked hand in hand. My trusted friend, Michael, told us to grab onto his wings, and we flew that night as angels.

Michael was the most difficult to say goodbye to. Somehow, I knew that he would always be my personal angel. As we hugged and I wouldn't let go, Michael smiled and said, "G-d speed, Yoseph." And then he was gone.

Marcia and I entered the house. It seemed like a morgue compared to the joy and laughter we had left behind at the banquet. Life would never be the same. I would give anything to turn back the clock, but I knew that I could neither stop nor reverse time. Only G-d has that power. He comes from a place where time does not exist. All we humans have is our memories. You have to take the bad with the good. It's the nature of things.

The stillness of the house was eerie. Marcia and I were too tipsy to stay awake. I just wanted to collapse on the bed and fall asleep. I should have been the happiest person on earth, but I was sad. Heaven was no more. I felt like Dorothy asking the Wizard how she would get back to Kansas. I said to Marcia:

*Yoseph:* How do we get back to Boynton Beach?

Little did I know that she was going back to Florida without me. My destiny lay elsewhere.

# Tomorrow

# 22

# ISAIAH

*M*ICHAEL HAD RETURNED in the still of the night and transported a heavenly, sleeping Marcia back to Florida. When she awoke the next morning, she found a note telling her that the Messiah Interviews were not over. She was told not to worry and that I would be safe.

The last thing I remembered was my head hitting the pillow. I found myself smiling, as I was dreaming in color for only the second time in my life. However, it wasn't a dream. I was under the spell of a prophetic vision. My angelic interviewer, Gabriel, was taking me into the future. We seemed to be flying at warp speed, as it was only a matter of minutes until we arrived at our destination. It now all made sense. At the end of our banquet in heaven, Gabriel was the only one who just waved and never gave me a hug goodbye. He knew that he would see me again. But where were we? We seemed to have landed on a high mountain.

Gabriel sensed my thoughts. I shall give you a hint. About 2,500 years ago, I stood in this very same place with the prophet Ezekiel, with my rod and linen cord.

*Gabriel:* Look, Yoseph, there is the city to the south that Ezekiel and I saw.

I turned and gazed. Chills were running up and down my spine, and yet my body wasn't cooling from the perspiration of a flu episode. Jerusalem, the city to the south, which will take on a new name in Messianic times: "G-d is there." G-d had instructed Gabriel to assist Ezekiel in taking the measurements of the future Temple on earth. Ezekiel was to teach the Babylonian exiles the measurements so that when they returned to Israel they would be able to expediently build the Messianic Temple. Gabriel would accomplish this with his cubit measuring rod and linen cord.

The returning Jews never built the final Messianic Temple, which would once again house G-d's Divine Presence. They constructed a Second Temple that resembled Solomon's First Temple, incorporating some features of Ezekiel's design. Ezekiel's Temple, the Third Temple, had undisclosed mysteries that only Elijah would explain in the End Times.

G-d's *Shechinah* was never destined to reside in the Second Temple. Neither was the Second Temple destined to stand eternally. It was destroyed by the Roman General, Titus, in 70 C.E. The date coincided with the official beginning of the religions of Judaism and Christianity, and also marked the end of Jewish tenure in the Land of Israel. Almost 1,900 years later, the Jews of the modern State of Israel retook Jerusalem. The day after the Six-Day War, Yinnon and I were standing in an Arab backyard gazing on a tiny wall—the Western or Wailing Wall of the Second Temple. Quite remarkable!

As we stood at the Eastern Gate, I turned around, and with my surgically treated cataract eyes, I gazed over the idyllic gardens of the Temple Mount into the distance to visualize a majestic heifer. This was not just any heifer, Gabriel explained. This was a Red Heifer, whose ashes were used by the High Priest for purification of contaminated souls. The Red Heifer appeared like the magnificent, wild white stallion in the movies, leading his herd of thoroughbreds and daring the cowboys to chase and catch him.

Of course, who should be there to greet us? It was none other than the gatekeeper, Elijah, the prophet. Elijah had disguised himself as a *Wizard of Oz* munchkin when Yinnon and I first approached the Third Temple in heaven. I chuckled at the memory of his outfit. He wore a purple, striped, short-sleeved Polo shirt over a long-sleeved, orange sweater and a Mickey Mouse red tie with a Stony Brook tie tack. His green, camouflage shorts were held up by rainbow suspenders, and his calves were covered with red and white striped socks. His outfit was topped off by a narrow and tall Dr. Seuss black-and-blue hat.

Magically, a munchkin no longer, Elijah now appeared as I had seen him last night at our banquet. He was almost as tall as me, and he was anything but impish. He was handsome and distinguished, with a salt-and-pepper beard and a head of hair that I envied.

The three of us walked through the deserted Outer and Inner Courtyards. We climbed the steps, and we once again entered the Sanctuary, a duplicate of the Sanctuary in heaven. There were three cushioned chairs, and I was instructed to sit in the middle while Elijah sat on my right and Gabriel to my left. In front of us stood the Menorah, the Showbread Table, the Incense Altar, and beyond was the Holy of Holies. The oil lamps of the Menorah burned bright, the incense odors permeated the room, and the *challahs* were visibly noticeable in the Showbread Table. The problem was that no one else was here. I turned to my companions, who shrugged and told me to be patient. I remembered the quote from my High School yearbook, "Patience is a virtue." On the outside, I was a patient person. My mother's impatience, however, had been imprinted into my neural pathways.

After about ten minutes in a semi-meditative state, Elijah got up, went out into the Hall, and gathered up another chair, which he placed facing opposite to us. At that moment, a man in white, whom I hadn't seen before, entered the Sanctuary and sat down in front of us.

*Isaiah:* Do you know who I am?

*Yoseph:* No.

*Isaiah:* I am like Elijah, and I'm not like him. Can you solve the riddle?

Like Elijah? I didn't like the way this interview had commenced, if it was an interview. Not waiting for my answer, the man spoke:

*Isaiah:* Elijah and I are prophets. Can you now solve the riddle?

He said that the answer lay in the words he has spoken. I searched my brain. The word *riddle* was the clue. Isaiah prophesied in poetic riddles. I felt like I was in a fairytale facing Rumplestiltskin, and I was about to divulge his name.

*Yoseph:* With all due respect, you are Isaiah.

*Isaiah:* Yes, Yoseph, I am the prophet Isaiah, and G-d has chosen me to interrogate you. All of the Messiah Interviews have you playing Scrooge in Charles Dickens' novel, *A Christmas Carol.* Your past, present, and future have become one.

You see, Yoseph, everyone for centuries has tried to guess the identity of the Messiah and the time of the End. Yet, none have ever connected the obscure riddles of the Hebrew Bible to the Messiah. This is essential, because the riddles offer the only clues as to who the Messiah really is.

G-d intended to mystify the Messiah, as He instructed Daniel to obscure the matters and seal the book. Just as He confused Jacob's mind on his deathbed when he was about to disclose the End Time to his twelve sons. G-d has intentionally done all of this until the appointed time, which is still not now. Even this, what you are witnessing, is not your present in the future. It is the future of the future, as it is yet to happen.

Do you understand, Yoseph?

*Yoseph:* Yes, I think I do. What you are saying is that I must solve all the riddles relevant to validate my claims to be the Messiah. Only then, if I am an identical match, like a bone marrow transplant, will I be chosen.

*Isaiah:* Correct. The first riddle to solve, you already have alluded to. It is Jonah slaying the Leviathan sea monster for a banquet of the righteous. This is one of the toughest riddles of all, and I shall give you a hint. The story is a metaphor. Yoseph, are you an incarnate of Jonah?

*Yoseph:* (Nervously) How much time do I have?

*Isaiah:* As you once told the dental student who asked, while you were proctoring one of their many exams, "We transcend time on my watch. Neither this exam nor any exam that I proctor has standard time limits." The Department of Oral Biology exams were supposed to have a limit of two hours. You never adhered to that time frame. Your generosity to the dental students in allowing them three and even four hours to complete their exams is now coming back as a gift from me to you. I extend you the same courtesy. There are no time limits. Answer whenever you are ready.

These Princes, angels, and prophets, not only read my mind. They know all of my past thoughts and actions. No wonder prophecy had to be abandoned by G-d, at the time idol worship was extinguished from the hearts and souls of the Jewish people. The continuation of prophecy would have been too powerful in a world of free will.

I pondered, thought, reflected, and could not solve the riddle. It wasn't like going through the alphabet, searching the letters, when you've forgotten a name. A name, which is there right on the tip of your tongue but you just can't quite remember. There was nothing in the riddle that I could exploit for my answer. The mindsets of Isaiah and I might just as well have been on different mountains. I had sought to play in this game, and now the cobra had struck the first blow.

I remembered a quote of a biblical commentator that says, "The most objective people have their own blind spots. Where their own interests our involved, they see things only a certain way." I had to think out of the box, look beyond myself, in this particular riddle. Isaiah's use of the word *metaphor* was the clue. There had to be a more general answer. I reasoned that I should be able to come up with a solution. G-d had come into, and saved, my life with Divine Providence. His gift would permit me to overcome seemingly impossible obstacles.

Jonah had survived inside a large fish for three days and three nights, and this was a miracle. The only connection to the riddle was that Jonah's experience took place in the sea.

I thought back on my life. I had been in tighter jams. Here, all I could lose was the chance to be the Messiah. In life, I almost lost my life. I had been through darkness, and I could appreciate the transformation of this darkness into light. So could Isaiah, who had a shortened life, living only forty years. Manasseh, a wicked idol-worshipping king of the Ten Northern Tribes, had him murdered in the Temple.

The infinite *Ein Sof* Light of the Temple was glorious, and I suddenly felt an infusion of G-d's strength. The Light seemed to be telling me not to give up my journey, not to surrender my fate.

It is said that G-d renews the *Ein Sof* Light to the world each year at the time of Rosh HaShanah, the Jewish New Year. Thus far, the actions of man have been undeserving, and G-d, fortunately for humanity, has acted patiently with mercy and benevolence to continue the Light. Should the Light ever be withdrawn, then we shall return to the nothingness, from which He created us and our universe.

I remembered Isaiah's own words about the Messiah in *Isaiah 42:4*: *"He shall not fail or be crushed until he sees right in this world."* And Solomon's words in *Proverbs 10:25*: *"A just man is the foundation of the world."* What I needed now was my intangible faith. I would do my best, but no matter how good my answer might be, the outcome would depend upon G-d. I also knew that being a showman was not the right course. My words had to be sincere to touch Isaiah's heart. There could, in fact, be more than one solution.

I looked up at Isaiah, who was patiently waiting. He smiled at me, as if he was signaling me that I would be okay, and I began.

*Yoseph:* The sea monster is a metaphor for the evil inclination that exists within all of us. Jonah's killing of the Leviathan is symbolic of the disappearance of the evil inclination at the End of Days. I have yet to defeat my evil inclination, like Jacob squarely beat Esau's angel. However, I vow to you and to the Creator in this Holy Chamber of the Third Temple that I shall do everything in my power, including more prayers and kind deeds, to be ready to be the Messiah at the End of Days.

I have already had my banquet in heaven with righteous men and angels, so perhaps I am 80 percent to 90 percent of the way to eliminating my own Leviathan. The residual may necessarily have to be removed at the End of Days, as G-d has promised to purge and cleanse the hearts of those admitted.

*Isaiah:* Your answer was direct and creative. Above all, it was sincere and spoken with humility. And now the second riddle. You have earlier answered one riddle regarding the duration of the Messianic Age. You have intelligently combined my verse on the life of a tree with Daniel's reference to years. Can you now explain Daniel's reference to, *"A time, times and a half?"*

Isaiah wasn't the only one who spoke in riddles. Daniel was pretty good in his own right. His dreams and visions were full of riddles.

*Yoseph:* Yes, in my own way. About six years ago, I began thinking about the Messiah when I wrote my first book, *Divinely Inspired*. What Daniel's words meant to me then, and still do today, is that *time* represents my generation; *times*, my twin sons generation; *and a half*, my grandchildren's generation. Six years ago, I had only one grandchild, Sarah. Today, I have Ethan.

Other interpretations have been put forth, but this is mine. Only Daniel and the Creator can tell us what the words mean.

*Isaiah:* I hadn't heard that explanation before. For the time being, I'll buy into it. Let's switch to the prophet Zecharia's riddle in *Zecharia 9:9*: *"The Messiah is triumphant and victorious, lowly and riding upon an ass, even upon a colt of the foal of an ass."*

*Yoseph:* The definition of a colt is a young male horse or a youthful inexperienced male. A foal is a young offspring of an equine animal, especially when under a year old. An ass is one of the hoofed animals of the genus *equus*. The term is closely related to horses and zebras, and includes the domesticated donkey.

The sages have interpreted that Zecharia was referring to the Messianic Age coming slowly in G-d's appointed time.

Zecharia's implied meaning might signify three generations of the Messiah: mine, my twins', and my grandchildren's. I prefer, still, another explanation. The donkeys and horses also could represent three generations of poverty. I know from my

upbringing what it's like to come from three family generations of being poor, and I also know more comfortable days
as a result of hard work in my life. As the Messiah, I would be
king of all the people because I am one of them.

*Isaiah:* Very interesting. However, how do you reconcile your interpretation with Daniel's words in *Daniel 7:13*?
*"Behold, with the clouds of heaven came one unto a son of
man, and he went to the Ancient One and He was brought
near before Him."*

The sages have interpreted Daniel's vision as signifying
that, in contrast to Zecharia's suggestion of a slow time period
until the Messianic Age, the Redemption at the End of Days
can come quickly, if we are but ready.

*Yoseph:* If I am going to apply Daniel's statement to me, I
will need to break the words up into two separate thoughts.

I too have seen visions in the clouds. G-d has placed
photographs of me ranging from how I looked as a child to
how I appear as an old man in the sky. I won't be so bold as
to suggest that theses heavenly photos represent the lifetime
of an individual destined to be the Messiah, but I do know I
have a connection to the Messianic Age in some way. There is
no doubt in my mind about that.

Secondly, during the recent time period that I was having
my miraculous womb experiences, I was wide-awake one night
and found myself levitating as if I were brought by angels
before G-d.

*Isaiah:* Do you have the audacity to suggest that Daniel's
vision was of you? Your appearance is not one of a sixty-seven-
year-old man. G-d did not show you in the sky as maintaining
your youthfulness into old age.

*Yoseph:* You are correct. G-d showed me in my natural state, in flashes of generations of an old man without hair. I wear a hairpiece, because of the effects of the neurotic damage of my upbringing. I wrote about this in *Divinely Inspired*, and I won't bore you with the sad details.

As to your comment about Daniel seeing me in the clouds, we don't know exactly the appearance of the Messiah, seen by Daniel. I was trying to make an analogy that I, too, have experienced miracles and visions in the clouds. If I am to be selected as the Messiah, and that's a big *if,* then it's quite possible that Daniel could have seen my face in the clouds. I was not being arrogant, and I apologize if you took my answer to be audacious. Only G-d can tell us whether the two experiences, Daniel's and mine, are related and are not a coincidence. Again, I'm sorry. The sages original explanation may be correct, and I just may be blowing smoke.

I think that Daniel's vision and Zecharia's prophecy refer to one and the same person, even if that's not me. You may believe Daniel's visions and not my levitation experiences in Primal Therapy. That's your privilege. However, you can see into my heart, and you know that I am telling you the truth.

We have yet to discover all the mysteries of the universe. And those that are legitimately discovered, like UFOs, are sometimes covered up by government.

*Isaiah:* Did you ever smoke marijuana?

Isaiah was all smiles. I thought, "What does his question have to do with the blue moon?"

*Yoseph:* Yes, I smoked when I was a postdoctoral fellow and assistant professor at New York University Medical Center. The period lasted between 1969 and 1973, and the marijuana smoking was very infrequent. Traveling on the New York subway system in rush hour back to my apartment in Flushing, after a stressful day at the lab, wasn't easy, and I would sometimes unwind by smoking my water pipe while listening to music.

*Isaiah:* How do we know that your miraculous cloud experiences were not due to the hallucinations or delusions of your bipolar disorder? You did experience psychotic mania in the nineties and thought you saw all kinds of weird visions.

*Yoseph:* Because I am telling you so. I protest your question and its inference. I won't, however, give you the satisfaction of blowing this interview with my anger. You are going to have to beat me fair and square.

To the best of my recollection, I have spoken truthfully about G-d's gifts of Divine Providence to me. He saved my life, on more than one occasion. In late 1998 and early 1999, when I saw myself in the clouds, I was well and not ill from manic depression. The bipolar disorder had left me, never to return. It's now almost eleven years later, and I am free of this nasty beast. This period exactly coincides with my spiritual journey.

*Isaiah:* (Smiling) You have passed the test, Yoseph. If you were to have blown up in anger, you would have lost the game before you had a chance to score. You would have given me power over you. This interview is different from all your other interviews in heaven.

Think of me as a soccer goalie. I am the last person you have to get by. In this interview, I am your strongest of adversaries. I am not your friend or supporter, until you pass the test. G-d has given me this task, and I intend to honor His command. We can't afford to make a mistake in choosing the wrong person as the Messiah. You bring a lot of baggage with you, and we need to be absolutely sure that you are the one.

*Yoseph:* Thank you. I now understand the rules of this interview. You are not here as my friend. Well as Churchill so aptly defined appeasement, "It is feeding the sharks in the hope that you will be eaten last." I am not here to appease you, Isaiah. I respect your wisdom too much to suck up to you. No one, with the exception of the Creator, has given me anything I did not earn.

I want you to be tough on me. There is too much at stake to approve an amateur like me when there are so many intelligent professionals, both present and past, to choose from who can fill this slot. I met seven of them in heaven.

I'm only in this soccer match if G-d wants me to be His Messiah. Otherwise, I will take all my marbles and go home. The Creator has sent signals to me, which suggest that my fate lies with Him. I have a good life in Florida with Marcia and the family, but I often get down when I think about the meaning of my life. I believe I have a calling, and I have found my spiritual mission in life. I won't be a perfect Messiah, as my neurotic ego is bound to get in the way. However, I will always act with kindness and compassion, which are the Ways of the Creator.

*Isaiah:* Fair enough, Yoseph. Let's continue the interview. Let's turn to some of my own poetic verses. In *Isaiah 11:4*, I speak G-d's words, *"The Messiah will smite the tyrant with the rod of his mouth and slay the wicked with the breath of his lips."* I wrote this sentence 2,700 years ago. What do the words mean to you?

*Yoseph:* A tyrant is a ruler who exercises power in a harsh and cruel manner. In the End Times, the tyrant may be the Antichrist, or Daniel's Beast, who will lead the seventy nations against Israel.

In your verse, the rod represents G-d, as He can speak for us if He so desires. Words are actions in themselves, especially if they expose the tyrant for who he is and for all to see. Nine out of ten people follow a persuasive argument, irrespective of whether the truth is spoken. G-d's Truth shall be triumphant.

The breath is also G-d. The Creator breathed a living soul into Adam, and Adam became a human being. I won't fight Satan with a sword. I'll challenge him with the power of my Divine Soul. With G-d at my side, nuclear weapons of the enemy will be rendered ineffective.

*Isaiah:* You understand, Yoseph, that I am not ruling on any of your responses at this time. At the end of this session, there will be a tribunal of all interviewers to vote either approval or disapproval of you.

In *Isaiah 11:3*, I write, *"And he shall not judge after the sight of his eyes. Neither decide after the hearing of his ears."* Can you comment on the powers of the Messiah?

*Yoseph:* I have discovered in these interviews that my interviewers have an uncanny ability to read my thoughts, and even my past actions. However, only G-d knows the intention of the person's heart behind his thoughts and actions. G-d will grant this gift to the Messiah, so he won't have to rely on his five senses to judge a person. The Messiah will see right through any facade by looking into a person's heart and soul. The Messiah, I believe, will be granted Divine powers.

*Isaiah:* In *Isaiah 35:5*, we have, *"The eyes of the blind will be opened, the ears of the deaf shall be unstopped, then shall the lame man leap as a hart and the tongue of the dumb shall sing again."*

*Yoseph:* In biblical times, G-d in his mercy could extend your life, like He did with King Hezekia by delaying the time period until the king succumbed to his illness or died of natural causes. Job, for all his misery and suffering, had his lifespan doubled. Through the prophets, G-d provided the metaphysical force, which allowed the prophets to revive the dead.

In the Messianic Age, G-d will perform miracles, incredible even to Him. Silicone Valley will not be able, in any lifetime, to approach G-d's inventive powers, as the most advanced technology is no match for G-d's miracles. Those who enter the Garden of Eden will not have to live out their *eternal* lives with their physical handicaps. The implication is that mental illness, like bipolar disorder, schizoaffective disorder, and schizophrenia, will be cured, as will spinal neuromuscular terminal illness, autoimmune disorders, heart disease, and cancer.

*Isaiah:* Just to re-emphasize Daniel's vision, in *Daniel 12:1-3*, there will be eternal life, which you earlier compared to a life of a very old tree, as written in my verse, *Isaiah 65:22.* At what age do we enter the Messianic Age?

*Yoseph:* I believe that if I were to die now, G-d forbid, I would hopefully be resurrected at the age I am now. The same may hold for everyone who will be a part of this new world. In this way, there would be equality, as we would each still have hundreds of years to live. If you're a child, when this happens, then you begin at your childhood age.

Old age in Messianic times is not old age today. For the hypothetical reasons, I discussed earlier, Methuselah's age of 969 might be equivalent to age 100 in our modern generation. It seems as if our souls will pass when we are very old. The Messiah's children and their descendants shall live on, so that there will always be a Messianic king to serve G-d and the people.

*Isaiah:* I now come to a passage, which many have suggested to defy the laws of nature, *Isaiah 11:6-8: "And the wolf shall dwell with the lamb. And the leopard with the kid. And the calf and the lion and the fatling together. And a little boy (child) shall lead them. And the cow and the bear shall feed. Together, their young ones shall rest. And the lion and ox shall eat straw. And the suckling child shall play upon the asp's hole. And over the basilisk's den, the weaned child shall pass his hand."* Yoseph, you do not have to answer this question if it's too personal, as nobody to date throughout history has been able to explain my thoughts.

Ah, the riddle of riddles! Meat eaters lying with grass eaters. How is that possible? Lions devour lambs. G-d created them this way. The small child, of course, is the Messiah. An asp is anyone of several poisonous snakes, like the cobra, that strikes at you, even if you are minding your own business. The basilisk is a legendary serpent or dragon with lethal breath or glands. We generally think of giant lizards as dragons.

I paused. Isaiah knew that I had thought about this passage deeply, because the lion, calf, cow, ox, and bear were metaphors for my family— Kenneth, Melanie, Seth, Sean, Erin, Magnus, Karen, and Martha Jean. Bipolar disorder can create a wolf within a lamb, and it did temporarily in my family. Sean was a lamb, who was named after both my gentle maternal grandfather, Sam, and my not-so-gentle paternal grandfather, Wolf. My youngest daughter, Erin, has large dark brown eyes like a leopard. My son, Kenneth, was an August baby and is a Leo, symbolizing a lion. My daughter-in-law, Karen, loved cows at one point in her life. My eldest daughter, Melanie, gives you hugs like a bear. Martha Jean is strong as an ox. Seth has the face of a calf or cow, and Magnus a handsome goat. I hope that my family will forgive me for using these analogies, but I only see them this way when I think about Isaiah's poetic metaphor.

*Yoseph:* The small child could be me. I was weaned before birth, as breastfeeding was an anxiety-ridden nightmare. The basilisk's den represents the womb of my mother, full of the tortuous twists and turns of Primal Pain. I did run my hand over the cervix as I passed through, and sadly I did play on the asp's hole, the vagina, during sexual abuse by my mother. I enjoyed the sexual stimulation, I shudder to confess.

Isaiah glared at me, as if he was the one with leopard eyes. Momentarily, he let his guard down, smiled, and complemented me on an original, but, as he put it, quirky theory.

*Isaiah:* Let's change the pace a bit. We are in the future Third Temple on earth. Is this the exact spot where Abraham was to sacrifice Isaac, where Noah built an altar to G-d, where even Adam was born, prior to being transported east to the Garden of Eden?

Will the future Third Temple be located on the same site where David and Solomon built the First Temple, and Ezra and the Men of the Great Assembly, the Second Temple?

*Yoseph:* Yes, all of what you stated is true. The site will be on Mount Moriah, currently buried beneath the ground in archaeological time. In a physical, spiritual, or both physical and spiritual sense, Mount Moriah will be the tallest of mountains in Israel at the End of Days.

Modern-day Jerusalem will move twenty-five or so kilometers south and will be renamed, *Hashem,* or *"G-d is there."* The geography of the land around current Jerusalem would have to change in order to accommodate a thirty-six times expanded Second Temple Mount.

*Isaiah:* Who was the last living descendant of King David's lineage, and can you prove that you are of his ancestry? I am bringing this topic up again, because besides solving he riddles, all is for naught if you are not a member of David's family tree.

*Yoseph:* Unfortunately, I cannot as yet determine whether I am a descendant of the lineage. Thus far, I have traced my origins to my four grandparents being born in the Ukraine. The grandparents on both sides seem to be related to each other. I need to do more ancestral genealogy. My DNA has been analyzed.

In the Hebrew Bible, the last recorded Davidic kingdom descendant appears to be Anani, the seventh son of Elvenai, descended from Zerubavel, who was a leader in building the Second Temple. In the New Testament, in contrast to the Hebrew Bible, the lineage is continued for multiple generations, until we reach Joseph and his virgin birth son, Jesus. The Hebrew Bible is often referred to as the Old Testament.

I would like to point out if that David had fathered other children who are not recorded in the Old Testament, then the entire genealogical issue would become murky, and perhaps moot.

*Isaiah:* I'm afraid the lack of genealogical proof would disqualify you in my eyes. I don't know how the others will feel. I would guess the same as me.

Talk about my downhearted feelings in Primal Therapy. Isaiah's terse comment was the ultimate shocker. The finale of finales. I would become just an ordinary man on the street again. Once more, I would lose my chance to be really special. I was devastated.

I thought of G-d's words in Amos 3:2: *"You alone did I know among the nations of the earth. Therefore, I will hold you accountable for all your sins."* I had naively believed that G-d and I had this wonderful relationship, although I had never exchanged words with Him, and He had barely spoken to me.

Indeed, I had a swelled head, and my ego had driven my thoughts and actions into this travesty of justice. In one fell swoop, Isaiah had cut me down at the knees and humiliated me beyond belief. I could not find my voice. I was stunned. I felt the neurosis creeping in. I was helplessly alone. Both Gabriel and Elijah looked at me sympathetically, but I could not be consoled.

I had come through so much in my life. I had exposed all of myself, more so than the nudity of Adam and Eve. I had repented my sins, unlike Shimon ben Laksihi's description of the wicked who do not repent their sins, even at the Gates of *Gehinnom*, or Hell.

*Isaiah 42:4* states, *"He shall not fail or be crushed, until he sets right in the world."* Ironically, the author of those inspiring words was talking to me now; however, he wasn't talking about me in his quote. When we light Sabbath candles on Friday night, we purposely let them burn out by themselves, because the candles symbolize the Divine Soul, which can never be extinguished by another human being. Only G-d can do this. I felt that Isaiah had just snuffed me out.

For one brief angry moment, I thought that this was an attempt on Isaiah's part to vindictively destroy me. I was hoping it was a practical joke. After all, as a biblical commentator wrote, "It is an unpleasant part of human nature that we can sometimes dislike a person, who is obviously better and more successful than we are. He makes us look bad, he makes us suffer by comparison with him, he makes our desires look petty and our excuses seem foolish. Such a person, especially if he exercises his obligation to lead, becomes a nuisance and an enemy of the people, and he is hated." My namesake, Joseph, became that person to his brothers, Jacob's ten other sons.

Through my tears, I looked at Isaiah, and realized that the reverse was true. Isaiah was a leader of prophets. I was a schlemiel on an ego trip. I had convinced myself that G-d desired me to make a difference. My passion had ignited, and wild horses couldn't stop me.

How would I be able to face Marcia, who was so happy for me? Was it really over?

*Isaiah:* I sense your panic of desperation. The only hope, which I can offer you, is that G-d can overrule the verdict of the Messiah Interviews. Only He would know whether you are a descendant of King David. None of us ancient or even modern mortals can determine this genetic linkage with absolute certainty. Scientific DNA proof is not available, because we don't have King David's DNA, or mine for that matter.

*Yoseph:* Based upon what you just said, I still have hope, and I wish to continue the interview. Even if I could find an ancestral genealogical link through my maternal and paternal grandparents, I would accept nothing short of scientific DNA proof. Since we are in the realm of the impossible, the answer has to come from the Father of Faith.

*Isaiah:* Well, I was going to stop here. Malachi the prophet, in *Malachi 3:23*, spoke, *"Behold I will send you Elijah the Prophet."* Elijah is not usually here with me, when we come down to the final interview. Yet, he is sitting beside you. I am sensing the Creator, as did a blind Isaac with Jacob dressed in

Esau's clothing to steal Esau's blessing. G-d wishes for me to continue the interview.

Can you suggest a riddle in scriptures, which you are having difficulty interpreting?

*Yoseph:* Yes, I do have one, as a matter of fact. It comes from *Genesis 3:15, "I will put enmity between you (the serpent) and the woman, and between your offspring and her offspring. He will pound your head and you will bite his heel."*

*Isaiah:* Well, often the *he* is thought to be the serpent and the *you* Eve's descendant. However, these roles could be reversed, so that the *he* is Eve's descendant and the *you* is the serpent's offspring. Does this help you solve the riddle?

*Yoseph:* It helps, but I'm still not sure. I suggested that a good person's admission into the Messianic Age might depend on his moral character being good at least 77 percent of the time. Most people are essentially a mixture of good and bad, but maybe we should classify a bad person as being bad 77 percent of the time.

My mother falls into this lower grade scheme classification. Ghastly as it seems, Satan's descendant referred to in Genesis could apply to my mother. Not in terms of genetics but in relationship to character. On balance, my mother's bad traits dominated her good qualities.

Now, to answer the riddle, after my usual lengthy discourse. A man has one head, but a woman has two. The womb represents a second head, and as best as I could as a fetus, I pounded that head as it was pounding me. On the way out of the birth canal, my mother tried to hold me back, and in one last ditch effort, she grabbed at my right heel. She metaphorically bit at my heel.

*Isaiah:* Your guess is as good as any other candidate, thus far. I just thought of something. How will you blow the Messiah's *Shofar* at the End of Days? You are not skilled at doing this.

*Yoseph:* True. In 1983, Marcia and I did purchase a *Shofar* on our honeymoon in Israel. We also, some two years ago, purchased a beautiful larger *Shofar* from Maurice's Judaica shop in Delray Beach. We gave both of these to my son Sean. Sean has a natural talent for playing the trumpet, and I shall give him the honor of sounding in the Messianic Age at the End of Days. The *Shofar* marks the Jewish people's and the world's return to G-d.

*Isaiah:* I like this idea of your son, Sean, blowing the *Shofar*. Can you tell me, Yoseph, why David purchased the land for the site of the First Temple from Aravnah the Jebusite? Why, for that matter, did Abraham purchase the Cave of Machpelah in Hebron from Mamre the Canaanite, or Jacob purchase the land around the biblical city of Shechem from Chomer? Shechem is where Joseph was buried. Moses carried Joseph's bones out of Egypt, as a reward for returning Jacob's body to the burial site of the Patriarchs and Matriarchs, save Rachel, in the Cave of Machpelah. Why? G-d had already granted the entire Land to Abraham, Isaac, and Jacob.

*Yoseph:* To record the purchases for posterity in order to avoid the argument we have today with the militant faction of the Palestinians, who claim all of Israel as their homeland.

As fate would have it, the Cave of Machpelah and Joseph's tomb lie in the Palestinian West Bank. At the End of Days, all the Land of Israel will be apportioned equally among the united Twelve Northern and Southern Tribes, and the Messiah.

Palestinians and Israelis today have the opportunity to be brothers and live in peace. DNA analyses confirms the close genetic relatedness of the Palestinians and the Jewish people.

*Isaiah:* My last discussion point concerns the relevance of *Isaiah 53*, in supporting your efforts to become the Messiah. Christianity has embraced my words as Jesus becoming the Messiah. Past sages have endorsed my speech as referring to the Messiah. However, more recent scholars and rabbis speak about these verses as alluding to the nation of Israel and not the Messiah. What is your stance?

*Yoseph:* I do believe your words refer to the Messiah. The great sage, Maimonides, interpreted *Isaiah 53:2*: *"He grew up before him as a tender plant and as a root of a dry ground,"* as the Messiah who made his way in life, essentially without the support of a father and a mother. This statement may fit Jesus, but it is also dead on in relation to me. This verse also speaks, *"we should look upon him, nor beauty that we should delight in him."* If you recall my birth, I was not born with beauty. I came into this world ugly and shriveled. Remember my mother's words, *"Get that ugly baby away from me."*

In *Isaiah 53:3*, we find the words, *"He was despised and forsaken of men, a man of pains, and acquainted with disease, and as one from whom men hide their face, he was despised, and we esteemed him not."* In the birth room, the doctors and nurses gasped when they saw me. Instead of the innocence and beauty of a new baby, I grew up feeling inferior because of my ugliness. I have had much suffering to deal with, and my family looked up to me to help them make medical decisions. My academic background as a pharmacist, biochemist, nutritionist, and microbiologist, as well as my own personal experiences with mental illness, anxiety, and depression, are all relevant to your words that I am acquainted with disease.

I am using selected verses to bolster my case. Verses like *Isaiah 53:7*: *"He was oppressed, though he humbled himself and opened not his mouth, as a lamb that is led to the slaughter, and as a sheep that before her shearers is dumb; yea he opened not his mouth."* Your words support my case, although I must admit in a larger scope, they could represent Jesus. Jesus expressed himself as a marvelous orator. I never expressed my feelings, beginning from my time in the womb to throughout most of my life.

I would next like to quote your verse *Isaiah 53:10*: *"Yet it pleased G-d to crush him by disease, to see if his soul would offer itself in restitution, that he might see his seed prolong his days, and that the purpose of G-d might prosper by his hand."* G-d was not pleased that the Messiah's soul was crushed. He was pleased because the Messiah repented and was indeed helping Him with His decision to prolong the life of humankind. You help G-d by your actions while living, not by dying for the sins of mankind. I will do this by writing the *Messiah Interviews*, with my hand as you indicate.

Your last verse reads: *"Therefore I will divide him a portion among the greats, and he shall divide the spoil with the mighty, because he bared his soul unto death, and was numbered with the transgressors, yet he bore the sin of many, and made intercession for the transgressors."* I have bared my soul to all of you greats, and when I write the *Messiah Interviews*, I will go public for all to see, for the eternity. Jesus was not considered a transgressor by his many followers, whom he gathered. I am a transgressor by anyone's standards. Until now, I didn't realize that part of my purpose was to bear the sins of many. I have offered a plan for admission into the Messianic Age. Everyone who will be admitted is a transgressor, though they are more good than bad. Through the words I wrote in *Divinely Inspired* and soon the *Messiah Interviews*, I am interceding on behalf of transgressors.

That's all I have to say on this verse.

*Isaiah:* Thank you, Yoseph. This marks the completion of the interviews. It is appropriate that these interviews were carried out in the Third Temples in heaven and earth. The process now is for all nine interviewers, Gabriel, Methuselah, Seth, Chanoch, King David, Moses, Jacob, Abraham, and myself to meet and come to a decision on your wish to become the Messiah. Consider us to be the group of nine jurors, similar to your nine Supreme Court justices. The difference is that the justices make the final decision on a case. We, however, are advisory to the Creator, and His decision is final.

It is fitting that this decision will be made in this Sanctuary. Yoseph, remember the words in *Exodus 25:8*: *"And they shall make a Sanctuary and I may dwell among them."* And from my own words in I*saiah 56:7*: *"For My House is a House of prayer for all peoples."* I ask you to now leave the Temple with Elijah. He will know when to return for the decision.

*Elijah:* Come, Yoseph. The morning dew has passed, and you could use a walk, and sustenance for all the energy that you have expended.

Elijah grabbed my arm, and we walked outside of the Northern Gate into the Temple Mount. There in front of us was the same fruit drink stand, which also was stocked with falafel on pita bread. As my teeth sank into my sandwich, it reminded me of my Ph.D. stay

in Israel. I loved to buy falafel or lamb in pita from the skewers of the street vendors.

I thought of the Supreme Court determining my fate. Was my approval based upon a unanimous vote, a two-thirds majority, or a simple majority? Wouldn't it be funny if the nine wise men turned the tables on me and required seven out of nine, 77 percent? I wanted a Yes or No, up and down vote, and I wanted to know who voted for and against me. I was to find out that I was in no position to make any demands. The ruling was binding and could not be retracted or appealed.

# 23

# JURY AND JUDGE

*T*WO HOURS HAD PASSED and still no word from the Sanctuary on a verdict. Maybe this was good news. My emotions were flying up and down. Unbeknownst to me, the Princes were trying for a unanimous vote in my favor. Isaiah was the lone holdout, and Gabriel initially abstained, since he felt that humans should make decisions about their own kind. When G-d requested that Gabriel vote, Gabriel nodded affirmatively. Isaiah remained steadfast in his opposition. He felt that I had an answer for solving every riddle, which I thought was the whole idea. This was despite the fact that he liked my originality. Surprisingly, Isaiah wasn't upset about my genealogical King David lineage response, as he thought that tracing the family by ancestry, without DNA confirmation, was a flawed approach.

Speaking unseen, in a Voice, which quietly resonated throughout the entire Sanctuary, G-d shared His Thoughts with His loyal servants.

Creator: *Only an "A" vote shall have My approval. According to the "A" standard set up by Yoseph, he does qualify to be the Messiah based upon your 8 to 1 vote.*

*All:* Do you want us to convey Your choice to Yoseph?

Creator: *NO. He still needs to assist Me, by writing the Messiah Interviews. People need to know the rules of the game, Yoseph's suggestions, for admission into the Messianic Age.*

*More of the Jews need to believe and trust in Me as their Supreme Being. And more people, of all faiths and beliefs, need to search their hearts and souls for Truth. My wish is for the success of the sinners, who still have the opportunity to sincerely repent and follow in My Ways. I want humanity to be aware of the Shechinah Third Temple, where the majesty of heaven meets the glory of earth, and where I shall dwell forever. Yoseph has yet to fulfill this part of his mission.*

*All:* Do you want us to tell Yoseph that he is disapproved? It would be a similar response to what you instructed Ezekiel to tell the three Babylon exiled youths who sought Your help when they were refusing to bow down to a statue of Nebuchadnezzar?

Creator: *NO. We need to be as truthful with Yoseph as he was with us. We can't expect anything less of ourselves than we do of him.*

*All:* What then?

Creator: *Tell him that you jurors tentatively approve, and I do likewise, pending further developments of His mission. Tell him there are other candidates, whom I am considering, which is the truth. Tell him I will come to him when he calls on Me and that I will assist him. Instruct him to continue his mission and to publish his book on the Messiah Interviews. Tell him also of his need to spend more of his time in promoting awareness of the Third Temple. Finally, tell him that I thank him and that I love him like he loves Me.*

*After you give him the news, I will instruct Michael to return Yoseph to Marcia in Florida. I already have removed the relevant portion of her memory, so that she will not remember her time in heaven. I will do the same for Yoseph, except that I will place the memories of his time in the Third Temples in his unconscious. When he writes his book, it will be as if he is writing the Messiah Interviews from his imagination or his dreams.*

*My purpose in placing these proceedings in his unconscious state is that Yoseph is quite good at retrieving his buried unconscious memories into consciousness. He has had years of experience in Primal Therapy. Long ago, even before his birth, I placed him on his path. I purposely chose his parents and caused his lifelong neurosis and suffering to build his character. In a sense, I have partially controlled his free will and his destiny. Now, I desire these unconscious memories to gnaw at him, so that he will yearn for them and maintain his passion for the challenges ahead.*

I was called in and given the disappointing news. Everyone congratulated me. I had a tentative acceptance, which certainly was better than being rejected. I would have liked to meet G-d. My consolation was that it was so good to see everyone again. We made chitchat until it was time to go. It was harder this time to say goodbye.

I looked over my shoulder, and there was Michael, my trusted angelic friend. I grabbed onto his wings, and we flew back to Florida.

One more hug from Michael, where I couldn't bring myself to let go. He gave me a kiss on the cheek and departed to heaven.

Before I could rush in to see Marcia, I felt my head spinning while my entire body started to tremble. I began reverberating in forced bioelectric contractions like those I experienced when I connected to the exact energies of my deepest feelings in the womb. However, unlike the unconscious memories of the past that I first felt, lost, and then retrieved after 15 to 30 seconds following the reverberations, there was a complete loss of what transpired during the interview process. All of my memories were gone in a flash. When I walked through the door, it was as if I had never left. Marcia's lips were invitingly tasty, and her breath sensually exciting. I swept her into my arms with a newfound strength, the source of which is a mystery to me, still today. I was returning to a magical life, with a clarity and passion of purpose to fulfill my spiritual mission.

After a night's rest, I sat down to begin writing. I had a new idea for a book. I would title the book, the *Messiah Interviews*.

# ∾ ABOUT THE AUTHOR ∾

Dr. Jerry Pollock is a Bachelor of Science and
Master of Science in Pharmacy graduate of the
University of Toronto. He obtained his Ph.D. in
Biophysics at the Weizmann Institute of Science in
Israel in 1969, and then he went on to New York
University Medical Center as a Postdoctoral Fellow
and Assistant Professor for four years of training
in Microbiology. In 1981, at the age of forty, he became Professor of
Oral Biology and Pathology in the School of Dental Medicine at the
State University of New York at Stony Brook. He retired as Professor
Emeritus from Stony Brook in July 2006.

He is a transplanted Torontonian to New York, by way of Israel,
and a transplanted New Yorker to Florida, where he now resides with
his wife, Marcia.

Dr. Pollock combines his scientific background with his spirituality. He was prompted to write this book to share his faith, trust, and
love of God. The *Messiah Interviews* represents his humble attempt to
give back to the Creator.

CPSIA information can be obtained at www.ICGtesting.com
Printed in the USA
LVOW081231311011

252842LV00001B/8/P